TROUBLESHOOTING ELECTRONIC EQUIPMENT THE RIGHT WAY
Without Using Expensive Test Instruments

D1496473

TROUBLESHOOTING ELECTRONIC EQUIPMENT THE RIGHT WAY
Without Using Expensive Test Instruments

John Douglas-Young

PTR Prentice Hall, Englewood Cliffs, New Jersey 07632

Library of Congress Cataloging-in-Publication Data

Douglas-Young, John.
   Troubleshooting electronic equipment the right way without using
expensive test instruments / John Douglas-Young.
     p.   cm.
   Includes index.
   ISBN 0-13-554114-X
   1. Electronic apparatus and appliances—Maintenance and repair.
I. Title.
TK7870.2.D69   1993
621.3815′48—dc20   92-28265
                         CIP

Editorial/production supervision
  and interior design: *The Wheetley Company*
Prepress buyer: *Mary Elizabeth McCartney*
Manufacturing buyer: *Susan Brunke*
Acquisitions editor: *Bernard M. Goodwin*

© 1993 by PTR Prentice-Hall, Inc.
A Simon & Schuster Company
Englewood Cliffs, New Jersey 07632

The publisher offers discounts on this book when ordered in bulk quantities.
For more information, write

Special Sales/Professional Marketing
Professional Technical Reference Division, Prentice Hall
Englewood Cliffs, NJ 07632.

Printed in the United States of America
10 9 8 7 6 5 4 3 2 1

ISBN   0-13-554114-X

Prentice-Hall International (UK) Limited, *London*
Prentice-Hall of Australia, Pty. Limited, *Sydney*
Prentice-Hall Canada Inc., *Toronto*
Prentice-Hall Hispanoamericana, S.A., *Mexico*
Prentice-Hall of India Private Limited, *New Delhi*
Prentice-Hall of Japan, Inc., *Tokyo*
Simon & Schuster Asia Pts. Ltd., *Singapore*
Editora Prentice-Hall do Brasil, Ltda., *Rio de Janeiro*

CONTENTS

PREFACE

I am privileged to receive annual catalogs of test equipment from leading manufacturers, and I am always astounded by the superb technology of their instruments; technology which shows that our country is still far ahead in this area. And I am also envious, because these wonderful toys have staggering prices, far beyond my limited means!

Although it would be nice to have some of them, they are not for the most part troubleshooting tools. To use for troubleshooting a state-of-the-art oscilloscope costing as much as a BMW would be like using the BMW to deliver newspapers. Much simpler equipment, such as a bicycle, will do the job.

This book, therefore, is about "bicycles" . . . and how to "ride" them. The emphasis is on the analog and digital multimeters, the logic probe, and so on, which can be obtained from neighborhood electronic parts stores for a minimum expense. It shows how they work and what they can do. The only instrument featured that would cost more than $100 is the oscilloscope, which you would need to invest in if you were making troubleshooting your business.

Troubleshooting as a business can only be profitable if done efficiently. The technician must be able to identify the problem as quickly as possible. By comparison, the repair itself takes little time, but the possible profit from the job can soon turn into a loss if time is wasted getting to it. The first chapter of the book explains how the technician must use reasoning power to determine the cause of each problem, and shows how to do this in a professional way.

The unprofessional, needle-in-a-haystack, hit-or-miss ways of earlier radio servicemen frequently led to the baffling mysteries that made people coin the phrase that electronics was an art, not a science. But that was the result of not using a scientific approach. In science reason says that an observed effect must have a logical cause, and knowledge of the scientific laws that apply in each particular case make it clear what that cause must be.

In electronics, then, which *is* a science, *not* an art, your knowledge of its laws, and how they apply in each particular case, should lead you to the solution of every problem. This book shows the way, and underscores the last statement.

Each case begins by looking for clues, but if you are unfamiliar with the equipment, you are likely to miss important ones. This is when you need the manufacturer's manual or Sam's Photofacts. This valuable information is an essential troubleshooting tool in itself. The modern television receiver, VCR, or hi-fi audio system is too complex for most people without some sort of directions.

However, this book cannot be a substitute for such directions for every piece of electronic gear. It does not pretend to be. It shows you the professional way to use such information, how to make the most of your test equipment, and how to get results fast. The adage "time is money" was never truer than in troubleshooting. To save time and make money you must know the way equipment works, use effect-to-cause reasoning, and understand your test equipment, as explained in these chapters.

John Douglas-Young

TROUBLESHOOTING ELECTRONIC EQUIPMENT THE RIGHT WAY
Without Using Expensive Test Instruments

1

PROFITABLE
TROUBLESHOOTING

WHY PROFESSIONAL DIAGNOSIS IS ABSOLUTELY ESSENTIAL

Suppose two technicians have to fix two identical television sets, each with exactly the same problem. One does the job in one hour, while the other takes ten hours. Which technician is the more profitable? Easy, isn't it? I mean, suppose they are paid $20 an hour. Then the first man's time costs $20, but the second man's time costs $200. So which man will wind up owning the business, and which one is on his way out, unless he improves drastically?

We assumed, of course, that both men had had the same training in electronics, and were equally intelligent. So what does the first one know that the second does not? He knows that every effect has a logical cause, and that he can deduce the cause of the problem by reasoning from its symptoms. He does not have to emulate his cohort's needle-in-the-haystack method, and test every component until he finds what has failed.

This is not a real case, of course, but it should emphasize that time is money in troubleshooting. The more time you save the more profitable it becomes, whether you work for yourself or for someone else. This book shows you how to troubleshoot effectively.

BASIC TROUBLESHOOTING PROCEDURE

The basic steps in troubleshooting all types of electronic equipment are shown in Figure 1-1. Not all steps will be required in every case. The nature of the problem will help determine which steps to do. The first thing is to find out as much as you can about this problem. Your immediate source of information is the person reporting the trouble.

If this person is another technician you're in luck, because then you can expect a reasonably informed and coherent description of what went wrong. But usually you have to interrogate the owner of the equipment to find out what happened. Table 1-1 gives a basic list of questions you might ask.

TABLE 1-1   Failure Symptoms as Reported by Owner

Question	Answer
1. What is the problem exactly?	_____
2. In what way does it show up?	_____
3. Is it permanent?	_____
4. If not permanent, under what conditions does it appear?	_____
5. Has there been any abuse?	_____
6. Did the problem come on gradually or start suddenly?	_____
7. Did it happen when someone was using the equipment?	_____
8. Is this problem confined to one function, or does it affect others?	_____
9. Can you offer any other information?	_____
10. Did anyone try to repair it?	_____

NOTES ON THE QUESTIONS

1. This is to try to get a better description of the problem than "it doesn't work," or "it's acting up." Quite often, the answer to this question will point to the part of the equipment where the defect has occurred.

2. This question is supplemental to the first. It tries to bring the problem into sharper focus.

3. Here you are trying to establish whether this is a complete failure of something, or whether it is something like a poor connection.

4. If the problem is intermittent, you would like to know if anything makes it happen (such as the operation of another piece of equipment nearby).

5. This question asks if the equipment has been subjected to shock, vibration, heat, or other stress.

6. If the defect came on gradually, it may be due to the aging of a component; if the defect was sudden, it suggests a catastrophic failure.

7. If the answer is yes, you might be able to get some idea of how the defect occurred—for instance, a sudden current surge on turn-on, or a turn-on with one of the controls set in an extreme position, and so on.

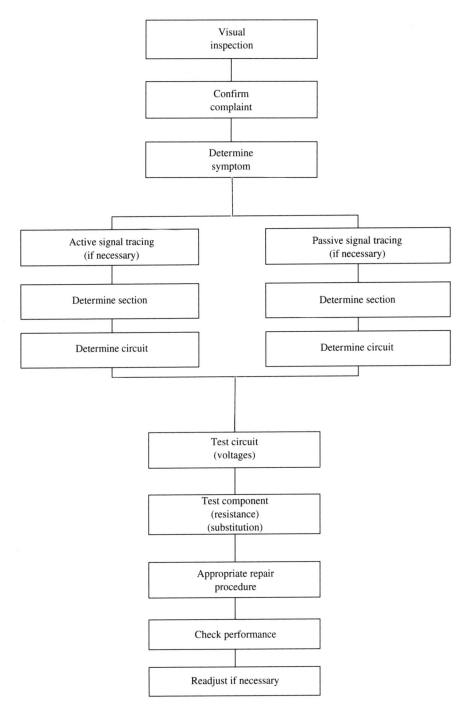

Figure 1-1 Basic Steps in Troubleshooting

8. If more than one function is affected, it might lead you to consider whether the problem is in another section that is common to both areas, such as the power supply.
9. Additional details would be such things as: a TV problem occurs only on certain channels; only one stereo channel is distorted; and so on.
10. If someone else has already worked on the equipment, you may have *more* than one problem to solve, and the original defect may now be masked by an effect of the unsuccessful repair.

Manufacturer's Manual and Other Data

The next step is to get the service data for the model you are preparing to troubleshoot. Actually, the best data package may be one obtained from a technical service company, such as Sam's Photofacts, since it is designed for troubleshooting. The main advantage of the manufacturer's material is that it is free.

Of course, if you are thoroughly familiar with the electronic equipment you are about to troubleshoot, and you know what all its parameters should be, you don't need these data. It's already firmly recorded in your mind, so you can pass immediately to the next step, which is the first one shown in Figure 1-1.

Visual Inspection

This is a quick look at the equipment, watching for any obvious physical or electrical damage, which may point straight to the cause of the problem. For instance, if its owner said that he saw smoke coming out of it so he shut it off, you would be looking for signs of overheating. Your nose could be a great help here! In most cases this inspection will reveal nothing, but it is worth doing because of the great saving of time that would result if you did see something. It only takes a minute or two, anyway.

Confirm Complaint

This means to try out the equipment to see what it does, if it is still in operating condition, and to make sure the complaint is as described by its owner. This is a good time to check the power supply (fuse, circuit breaker, or fusible resistor, if it has one), or the battery (especially the battery!).

Effect-to-Cause Reasoning

This is the most powerful technique of all, yet it does not even exist in physical form. It is, however, very familiar to all of us. It is the power of reason.

We use it all the time in daily life. We flip the light switch on the wall. Nothing happens. We jiggle it a few times, still with no result. Then we try another light switch in another room. This light turns on, so we reason that it cannot be a power failure. Next, we unscrew the bulb, and substitute another, but still without result. Now we reason that there is no power in the circuit in question. We therefore go to the power distribution box, and check the circuit breakers. We find the one for this circuit has tripped. When we reset it the bulb lights.

This is a simple example of effect-to-cause reasoning. The bulb did not light (the effect). We reasoned that this had to be due to lack of power (the cause). There were, however, three things that could remove the power: an external power outage, a tripped circuit breaker, or a malfunctioning switch. The bulb could have been bad also. In each case we deduced a possible cause from the effect observed. By eliminating them one by one we arrived at the actual cause.

In troubleshooting electronic equipment it is not always so easy to understand the relationship between cause and effect. It is essential to have a firm grasp of the principle of operation of all parts of the equipment in question. But given this, it is sometimes possible to locate the cause of the trouble by reason alone, without the use of any other test equipment.

Figure 1-2 shows a simple stereo set with inputs from two antennas, a phonograph, a tape player, and, of course, a power supply. It also has a motor that drives the phonograph turntable. It has outputs to two speakers.

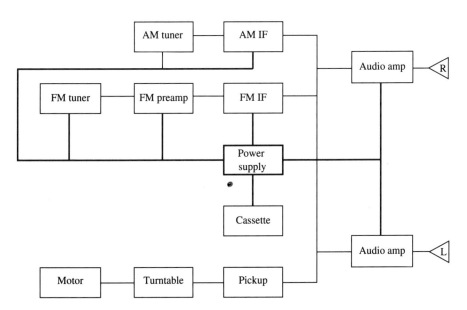

Figure 1-2 Simplified Stereo Block Diagram

Table 1-2 shows how various groups of symptoms point to the section where the problem lies. This table does not give all possible symptoms and defective functions, but just a selection so you can see how this works.

TABLE 1-2   Effect-to-Cause Reasoning for Stereo Set

Symptom	Defective Section
Turntable doesn't turn AM and FM sound working Cassette player working	Motor
No phono sound AM and FM sound working Cassette player working	Phono pickup or preamp
No phono sound No AM sound No FM sound No cassette sound Turntable turns	Power supply
No FM sound All other sections okay	FM tuner, preamp, or IF amp
No sound from one speaker Other speaker is okay on all functions	That speaker's amplifier
No sound when cassette function is selected All other functions okay	Cassette player

In order to use effect-to-cause reasoning efficiently you must understand how the equipment works. This is where the manufacturer's data, or similar information, comes in. The real value of reasoning from effect to cause is in localizing the problem fast, and not wasting time chasing will-o'-the-wisps in the wrong parts of the system. But you can do this only if you understand the functions performed by each section of the equipment. You have to observe the symptoms and know which functions are associated with them.

Determine Symptom

This involves careful evaluation of the symptom. Make sure it is what it appears to be. Snow and spark plug interference can look similar on a TV screen, for example. However, snow is totally random; spark plug interference has a pattern to it, and only occurs when a vehicle is passing.

Determine Section

Of course, sometimes the same symptom may be caused by more than one section. A dark TV picture tube might be the result of a failure in the high-voltage section, the horizontal sweep system, the tube itself, or a misadjusted brightness control. In this case you would narrow it down quickly by checking the brightness control, by a glance at the neck of the tube to see if its filament was lit, and by the presence of high voltage (with a neon bulb tester). One of these would indicate the area of the problem, and you would be able to get to work on the next stage.

Test Circuit

A piece of electronic equipment may consist of many sections, or only one. A TV set has many sections, an AM radio only one. Each section may have many circuits, or consist of a single circuit alone. Except in the latter case, you still have to find the circuit where the trouble is originating.

If you have not already done so, begin by checking the power supply. A great many problems are cured by a fresh battery. But even in an electronic power supply, components can age or fail, because they are often under greater stress (from heat, higher voltages and currents, and so on) than anywhere else in the equipment.

The most powerful technique to use now is *signal tracing*. This means following a signal through the circuits of the section until you find the place where it is blocked, or drastically altered in some unwanted way. You may provide a suitable signal by means of a signal generator. This is called *active signal tracing*. Or you may use a signal that is already there (internally generated, or received from the preceding section). This is called *passive signal tracing*.

Active Signal Tracing. You can apply active signal tracing in two ways. Figure 1–3 shows the first way, signal tracing in an AM radio. Couple an AM generator to the antenna. In an AM radio this is a ferrite rod with two coils wound on it, so wind a wire a couple of times around the rod, and connect the generator lead to that. Then turn on the AM generator, and select a frequency in the AM band at a point where there is no strong local station to interfere. Modulate it with a suitable audio frequency (say, 1 kilohertz).

If everything is working properly you should hear the modulating tone in the loudspeaker. If you do not, disconnect the AM generator from the antenna, and reconnect it to the point marked *A* between the converter and the IF amplifier. The frequency must now be changed to the intermediate frequency of 455 kilohertz, as if the signal had passed through the converter. If you hear the tone now, the problem must be in the converter.

If you do not hear the tone, reconnect the lead to point *B*. Again, if you hear nothing, go to point *C*. At this point the signal should have changed to an

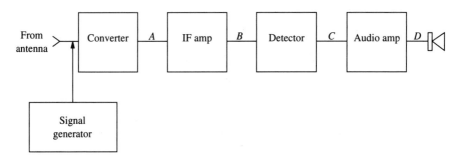

Figure 1-3   Active Signal Tracing in an AM Radio

audio frequency, so you need an audio generator (unless the AM generator can furnish the audio frequency). If nothing happens now, you are left with the speaker as the only place the defect might be.

Incidentally, it would obviously be necessary to increase the strength of the signal as you progressed, to compensate for the diminishing amplification it would be getting as the injection point approached the speaker.

Signal tracing can also be done in the opposite direction, by starting at point D and working forward. In this case you would know you had found the defective circuit when something happened to the signal. You would also need to change the frequency of the AM generator, and reduce its output as you moved through points of injection D through A.

Passive Signal Tracing.   In the case of a radio, as in many other circuits, you can manage without a signal generator if a strong local station is available. The procedure is the same, but in this case no test equipment is needed. You can go in either direction. However, if you first take a screwdriver or test lead, and ground the signal path at point B between the IF amplifier and AM detector, you can tell at once which half of the equipment is defective. A pop in the speaker will prove that the detector and audio amplifier are working, silence will show that one of them is not. In the first case, you will know the defect is in the amplifier or the converter. In the second, ground the input of the audio amplifier, and if there is still no pop, you know that the audio amplifier is not working.

These simple examples explain the signal tracing technique. In some cases you actually do not require any test equipment at all. The video screen or speaker, together with your eyes and ears, are perfectly adequate. However, in most cases you will use more complex equipment, such as a signal generator and oscilloscope, function generator and logic probe, and so on. Usually you need to know exactly what input signal you are applying to a suspected circuit, and what its output should be. To measure the latter you need a suitable piece of test equipment.

Test Component

When you have isolated the circuit containing the defect you will want to pinpoint the component at fault. This is generally done by measuring voltages and resistances in the circuit. Voltages are measured with the power on, *resistances with the power off.* The latter requirement is very important. You will not get much of a result trying to measure voltage with the power off, but you are likely to zap your meter if you try and measure resistance with the power on!

Voltage.   Most manufacturers' circuit diagrams indicate what the voltages for a properly operating piece of equipment should be at various points. For instance, in Figure 1-4 the data give the voltage between point A and ground as 8.9 V_{dc}, but you measure it as only 6.6 V_{dc}. Your suspicions turn to the capacitor C_1. If it were leaky, it would be loading the circuit. You turn off the power, and disconnect one end of C_1. Then you connect another of the same value, that you know is good, between point A and ground, and turn the power back on. The voltage at point A is now 8.9 V_{dc}, as it should be. This is called *substitution,* and we shall come back to it again shortly.

Resistance.   Measurement of resistance is used more than any other technique for testing electronic components. Apart from measuring the values of resistors, it is used to verify continuity in wiring, and components in which wire is the main characteristic, such as transformers. It can also be used for checking capacitors.

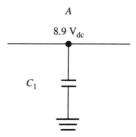

Figure 1-4 Substitution

Substitution.   Substitution is the clincher in troubleshooting. If yanking a component out and putting in a new one cures the problem, that's what must have been wrong. However, there are some pitfalls.

You must use an exact replacement wherever possible. While no harm is done in replacing a ¼-watt resistor with a ½-watt one, if there is room, it isn't advisable the other way around. The same applies to resistance tolerances. You should not replace a 5 percent resistor with a 10 percent one, unless you have verified by actual measurement that it is within 5 percent of the nominal value.

Even more care is required in replacing capacitors, since there may be a critical time constant situation as well.

Exact replacements of semiconductor devices (transistors, diodes, and so on) are not always available. Semiconductor handbooks give substitutes that will work, but it is a wise precaution to get the data for the original device and the proposed substitute, and read them side by side. In this way you will know whether the latter will work under the conditions in which it will be used.

In the case of most integrated circuits, only an exact replacement will do, and the same applies to most other special parts. Some of these claim to be equivalent to the original, but there is always some doubt about a much less expensive one.

In installing the new component into the circuit, you must be particularly careful to get its connections right. This sounds elementary, but you can be fooled. You can hardly see the markings on very small parts, like diodes, that must be installed with the correct polarity, so it is easy to make a mistake. A replacement transistor, or other semiconductor, may also have a different pin or lead arrangement.

When All Else Fails

It can happen sometimes that you will have gone through this entire troubleshooting procedure without isolating the defect. This may be because the malfunction is intermittent, and refuses to show itself when you are trying to find it. Such problems are discussed in Chapter 11. But if it is not intermittent, why wasn't it pinpointed by the foregoing procedure, in which apparently no stone was left unturned?

The wisest thing to do now is to do nothing. Put the equipment aside, and go on to something else. If possible, come back to it the following morning. A good night's sleep clears the mind, and you may then realize something you overlooked.

However, if nothing comes to mind, then do this. List on a piece of paper each troubleshooting step you did, and draw a simplified schematic of the circuit you determined to be at fault. Fill in the values obtained by your voltage and resistance checks. Then put your drawing beside the manufacturer's data, and make a careful comparison.

If that doesn't help, turn off the power in the equipment and proceed to check the continuity of all the *connections* in the circuit. Make sure that all connectors, including edge connectors of printed circuit boards, are firmly plugged in. Make sure that the pins of plugs and sockets are correctly mated.

Among the defects that can be most baffling to track down are poor solder connections. Visual inspection seldom shows them. If you think there is a chance that this may be the case in your circuit, it may save you much time and trouble if you apply your hot soldering iron to each such connection, so that the solder melts and resolders it.

A broken wire would not be noticed in a visual inspection if it occurs right at the point where it is connected, or at the place where the insulation has been stripped. Occasionally a wire will break within the insulation at a sharp bend. There is more about this kind of defect in Chapter 11.

Dirt and moisture can cause partial short circuits where uninsulated conductors are close together. On printed circuit boards short circuits can occur from the same cause, and also from what are called "solder hairs," which are fine strands of solder. Hairline cracks in the conductors can also occur, due to bending or expansion of the board. An open circuit like this can only be found by continuity tests, but shorts can sometimes be located by low-level voltage measurements, as described in Chapter 3.

Short circuits in the high-voltage sections of certain equipment such as transmitters and cathode-ray tubes may be caused by dirt, moisture, or sharp points from which corona discharges can take place.

Finally, it is always possible that a wrong component has been installed. If someone has worked on the equipment before, this may be the case. Although this is a question that should be asked when the equipment is brought in for repair, you do not always get a truthful answer. It is possible that the owner tried to fix it himself, and doesn't want to admit that it ended up worse than it was at the beginning. You should look for any components that look clean or new, and for anything else that is different from the manufacturer's style. Amateur soldering is at the bottom of many problems.

When working on any electronic equipment you must be mindful of your own safety, and the possibility of damage to the equipment itself. Electricity, like fire, is a good servant but a bad master; don't give it the chance to bite you. Keep in mind at all times the precautions outlined below.

SAFETY PRECAUTIONS

A voltage over 50 V_{dc} (25 V_{rms}) can be hazardous to your health.

A current of only 3 mA can stop your heart's operation (it need be only 10 μA_{dc} to burn your skin).

A frequency of 60 Hz is the frequency most likely to cause fibrillation of your heart.

These are medical facts, and should be borne in mind when working on any electronic equipment. If any of these hazards are present, it is unwise to work alone; someone else should be nearby who can render first aid if required (mouth-to-mouth resuscitation or CPR, for instance). Always keep one hand in your pocket to avoid the possibility of current passing through your chest area. Remember that a hand-held instrument or test leads can bring dangerous currents and voltages very close to you. Don't touch exposed wiring, connections, or other live parts. Don't use cracked or broken test leads. Use the correct power cord (in good condition), in a properly wired receptacle, with adequate ground if the cord has a ground prong. Do not operate in an explosive atmosphere. Never apply voltages that exceed limits given in the equipment's specification. Turn off power before connecting probes, and double-check switch settings and lead connections before turning power back on. Disconnect leads or turn off power before changing switch settings. Use fuses of correct type, voltage, and current ratings only.

SAFETY IS NO ACCIDENT

2

THE TRUSTY MULTITESTER

Although some tests can be done with no test equipment at all, you would not expect to do very many without at least one basic instrument, and that would be an *analog multitester* (AMT) or a *digital multimeter* (DMM). This chapter is about the AMT. The DMM is covered in Chapter 3.

Both of these are rugged hand-held portable meters that measure dc volts, ac volts, resistance, and current. The main difference between them is the way in which the value of the measurement is displayed. As you can see in Figure 2-1, the AMT has a dial and pointer. The angle of deflection of the pointer is proportional to the quantity being measured, so that its position against the dial indicates the value.

THE ANALOG MULTITESTER

Direct Measurement

The AMT is a direct-measurement device. That is to say, for measurements of voltage and current it draws such power as it requires from the circuit being tested. The core of an AMT is the *permanent-magnet moving-coil* (PMMC) meter movement, shown in Figure 2-2 (a) and (b).

The Permanent-Magnet Moving-Coil Meter Movement

The basic PMMC movement shown in Figure 2–2 (a) consists of a small coil of wire wound on a light aluminum frame, supported on jeweled bearings between the poles of a permanent magnet. Spiral hairsprings hold the coil so that its attached pointer is at zero on the dial scale. These hairsprings, similar to those in wind-up watches, are connected to opposite ends of the coil and conduct current to it.

When a current flows through the coil, its magnetic field interacts with that of the permanent magnet, so that a turning force is applied to the coil. The coil rotates until the opposition of the hairsprings just balances the magnetic torque. The pointer now indicates the corresponding value on the dial scale. When the current ceases to flow in the coil, the hairsprings return the coil and pointer to the zero position.

Within the coil is a stationary iron core. Its function is to maintain a uniform field in the space through which the coil rotates so that its motion will be linear.

Occasionally, it will be necessary to reposition the pointer over the zero mark. This is done by an adjustment on the front of the meter, just below the

Figure 2–1   Analog Multitester (AMT)

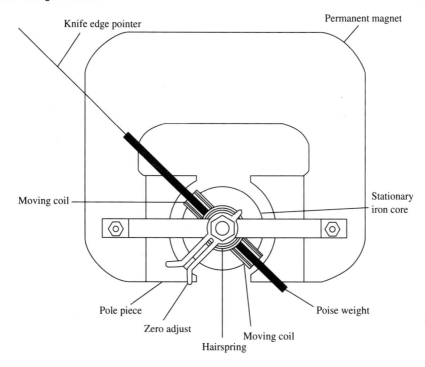

(a) Hairspring and Pivot Type

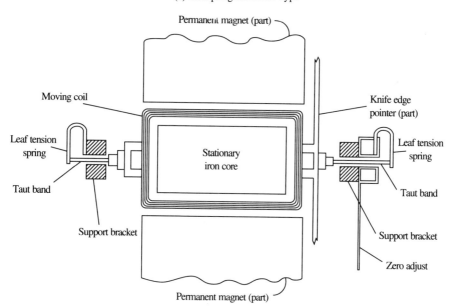

(b) Taut = Band Suspension

Figure 2-2 PMMC Meter Movement

dial, that resembles a screwhead, as you can see in Figure 2-1. Turning this adjustment with a small screwdriver rotates a peg that is located between the Y-shaped projections mounted on the support bracket shown in Figure 2-2 (a). This peg is offset from the axis of the screw, so that it turns in a circle, moving the Y-shaped projections first one way, then the other. One end of the front hairspring is attached to the opposite end of this projection, so that turning it changes the tension of the spring slightly, causing the pointer to shift its resting position.

The improved version, shown in Figure 2-2 (b), is called a *taut-band suspension movement*. The pivots, jeweled bearings, and hairsprings have been replaced by suspension bands made of a precious metal alloy that are held taut by leaf tension springs. When a current flows through the armature coil it rotates, twisting the suspension bands until their torque balances the magnetic torque. The magnetic torque is proportional to the current flowing in the armature coil, so the angle of rotation of the attached pointer corresponds to the value of the current. When the current ceases to flow, the suspension bands relax, returning the pointer to its zero position. This method of suspension eliminates friction between pivots and bearings and is more rugged and durable than suspension with hairsprings, although the latter is still widely used.

Meter Characteristics

The manufacturer of a PMMC meter will give its specifications in the following form.

Accuracy	± 1.0%
Repeatability	0.5%
Friction	0.2%
Damping Factor	2
Response Time	2 sec max
Overshoot	25%
Tracking	± 0.5%
Temperature Influence	± 1%/10° from 25°C
Frequency Influence	Flat from 15 to 10,000 Hz
Position Influence	1.0%

These are the principal characteristics of the meter. They are always the same for every meter, of course, but vary somewhat, depending upon the type. You ought to have some idea of what they mean, because they can tell you how suitable the meter is for your purpose.

Accuracy is the measure of how close the meter reading is to the true value of the applied energy. It is usually given as a percentage of full scale. For example, if a meter with a scale reading of from 0–100 milliamperes always reads between 99 and 101 mA when a 100-mA current is applied to it, its accuracy is ± 1 percent. This meter will read within 1 mA of the true value at any point on the scale.

Repeatability is the measure of the meter's ability to provide the same reading every time for the same input. The figure is a percentage of full scale, so on a 0–100 V_{dc} scale, for example, 0.5 percent would mean that the pointer would come to rest within half a volt of the same scale reading each time for the same input.

Friction means the maximum percentage of the full-scale value that the pointer may move if you tap the meter after it comes to rest. (Does not apply to taut-band suspension meters.)

Damping factor is a ratio obtained by a sudden application of current to a meter so that it deflects to full scale before dropping back to a steady deflection. If the full-scale value is 100 V_{dc}, and the pointer drops back to 80 V_{dc} after the initial deflection, the damping factor *DF* is given by

$$DF = 80/(100 - 80) = 4.$$

The higher the figure, the more heavily damped the movement is.

Damping is a means of controlling the swinging back and forth of the movement when a current or voltage is first applied. In AMTs this is performed by the magnetic field in which the movement turns, and is called *magnetic damping*.

Response time is the time taken by the pointer to settle down after an abrupt change in the applied energy.

Overshoot is the amount by which the pointer overshoots when the applied energy is changed, and is expressed as a percentage of the deflection after the movement has come to rest.

Tracking means the ability of a meter to indicate accurately at each scale division. It is calculated by applying energy to give an exact full-scale deflection, after which the applied energy is reduced until the pointer is exactly over the next lower selected scale division, and so on down the scale. The actual values of applied energy for each deflection are noted. The manufacturer's figure will be a maximum error for any point checked.

Temperature influence means a variation in meter readings due to temperature alone. In this case it is expressed within one percent for every ten degrees from 25° Celsius.

Frequency influence is a change in the reading due solely to a change in frequency of the applied energy. The expression "flat from 15 to 10,000 Hz" means that frequency influence is zero between these limits. If a change is due to a change of waveform, it is called *waveform influence*. These two factors apply only to ac measurements.

Position influence means the amount of change, if any, when the meter is operated in different positions.

METER APPLICATIONS

The heart of an AMT is its sensitive PMMC movement. In the circuit in Figure 2-3 this is a 50-microampere movement, connected as a dc voltmeter, ac voltmeter, current meter, or ohmmeter by setting the function switch. (Note: this is *not* the circuit of the AMT in Figure 2-1.) This switch also selects ranges for each function. For this reason AMTs are also called volt-ohm-milliammeters, or VOMs. The dial has separate scales for different functions and ranges.

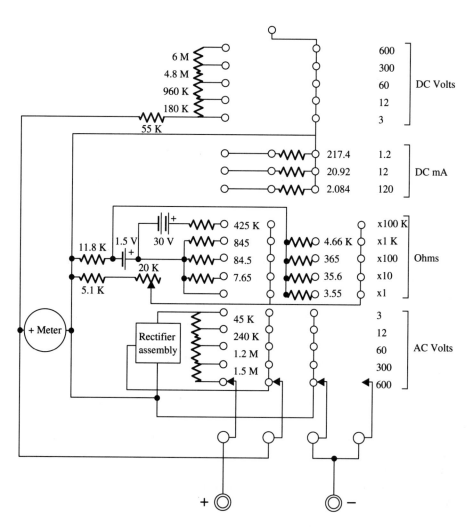

Figure 2-3 Typical AMT Circuit

Voltage Measurement

DC voltage measurements use the portion of this circuit shown in Figure 2-4. Various resistances are connected in series with the meter in accordance with the voltage range selected. These resistors are required to reduce the current applied to the meter to a value within its maximum current capability. The meter in this AMT has a maximum current capacity of 50 microamperes, and its internal resistance is 5,000 ohms. When the function switch is set to the dc range of 3 volts, R_1, a resistor of 55 kilohms, is added in series with the meter, to give a total of 60 kilohms resistance in the circuit. The current I_m flowing through the meter when 3 V_{dc} is applied to the input terminals is given by

$$I_m = 3 / 60 \times 10^3 = 50 \times 10^{-6} = 50 \ \mu A.$$

Obviously, if a voltage over 3 V_{dc} were to be applied to the AMT on this range, it would cause excessive current to flow through the meter, with probable damage to the movement. For this reason, if you are not sure of the voltage you are about to measure, *you should always set the function switch to the highest range first,* and then switch downward to the most convenient range.

In choosing the final range, it is best to use one where the readings will fall in the upper, or right-hand, half of the scale, for greatest accuracy.

The next higher range adds 180 kilohms to the total resistance, so that when the maximum voltage of 12 V_{dc} on this range is applied,

$$I_m = 12 / 240 \times 10^3 = 50 \times 10^{-6} = 50 \ \mu A$$

as before.

Additional resistances are switched in for higher ranges, as shown in the schematic diagram.

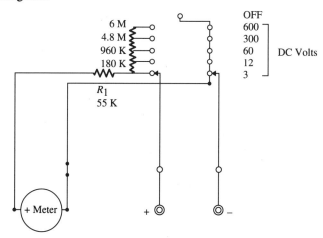

Figure 2-4   DC Voltmeter Section

On the dial three scales are used for the readings, with full-scale values of 12, 60, and 300. The 300-volt scale is also used for the 3-volt range, and the 60-volt scale for the 600-volt range.

On the lower part of the dial there is a statement that says: "OHMS PER VOLT DC 20,000 AC 5,000." This is important. It tells you the input impedance of the AMT. As you have just seen, on the 3-volt range the meter and series resistance add up to 60 kilohms. Dividing this by the full-scale value, gives 20,000 ohms per volt. This may make quite a difference in some circuits. Consider the case measuring the bias voltage on the base of a transistor, as shown in Figure 2–5. You can see that with the values given in the circuit it should be 0.625 V_{dc}. But when the AMT is connected between the base and ground, it reads slightly over 0.5 V_{dc}. This is because the 10-kilohm resistor in the voltage divider is being shunted by the combined internal resistance of the meter and the range resistor, which in this case add to 60 kilohms. The combined resistance between the base and ground is now only 8,571 ohms.

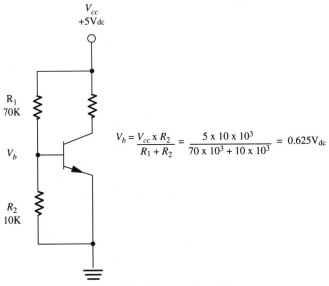

$$V_b = \frac{V_{cc} \times R_2}{R_1 + R_2} = \frac{5 \times 10 \times 10^3}{70 \times 10^3 + 10 \times 10^3} = 0.625 V_{dc}$$

Figure 2–5 What Loading Means

This makes the AMT less suitable for voltage measurements in low-voltage circuits than the DMM. This effect is less pronounced on the higher ranges, of course, because of the higher values of the series resistances. Also, because of its 20,000 ohms per volt impedance, this AMT is considered to be a sensitive one. Some have a rating of only 2,000 ohms per volt.

This disadvantage has been overcome in the FET-Input Multitester, where the use of field-effect transistors in the input gives an input impedance of 10 megohms. However, there still remains the difficulty of reading low voltages with sufficient resolution, for which you need the DMM.

AC Voltage Measurements are performed in a similar way, as shown in Figure 2–6, but the ac has to be rectified before it can be applied to the meter. To do this, a full-wave rectifier with two diodes is added. This causes a reduction of accuracy in ac measurements as the frequency increases above 60 hertz. The manufacturer may claim that the AMT is usable from 10 hertz to 500 kilohertz, but its ac accuracy of ±3% usually only applies to a 60-hertz sine wave.

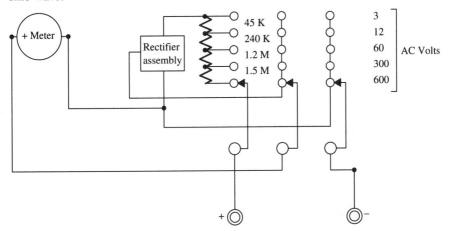

Figure 2–6   AC Voltmeter Section

The reason for the different values of the range resistors in the ac function is because the deflection of the movement is in proportion to the *average value* of the rectified wave. However, this is not the *root-mean-square (rms)* value that is normally used. The average value of a sine wave is 0.636 of the peak value, but the rms value is 0.707 of the peak value. At this level the sine wave contains the same energy as 1 V_{dc}. To make the AMT read in rms, the scale divisions are enlarged to 1.11 times the average value divisions. But this will be true only for sine waves. On other waveforms, the pointer will also point to 1.11 times the average value, but this will *not* be the rms value.

If you want to measure the ac portion of a voltage consisting of ac mixed with dc (as in the output of an audio power amplifier), you must connect a capacitor in series with the red test lead to block the dc. The capacitor should have a value of at least 0.1 μF, with a working voltage not less than the maximum voltage in the circuit.

Current Measurement

The section of the AMT for measuring current is shown separately in Figure 2–7. You will see immediately that whereas the range resistors for voltage measurements were connected in series with the meter, those for current are connected in parallel with it.

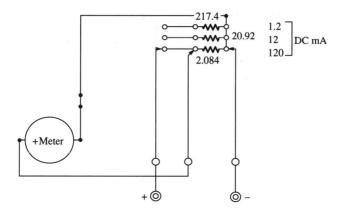

Figure 2-7 Current Meter Section

To see how this works, see what happens when you measure a current of 1.2 mA. The function switch is set to the DCMA range of 1.2 mA, and when the probes are connected to the current source, the pointer goes to full scale. Now the total resistance R_t in the circuit is given by

$$R_t = \frac{R_m \times R_{\text{shunt}}}{R_m + R_{\text{shunt}}} = \frac{5 \times 10^3 \times 217.4}{5 \times 10^3 + 217.4} = 208.3 \ \Omega.$$

Since the current is 1.2 mA the voltage V across the circuit is given by

$$V = 1.2 \times 10^{-3} \times 208.3 = 0.25 \ V_{\text{dc}}.$$

This gives a current I_m through the meter of

$$I_m = \frac{0.25}{5 \times 10^3} = 50 \ \mu A,$$

and a current through the shunt resistor of

$$I_{\text{shunt}} = \frac{0.25}{217.4} = 1.15 \ mA.$$

As you can see, the 1.2-mA current divides between the shunt resistor and the meter so that only 50 μA goes through the meter. The values of each of the other shunt resistors are chosen to bypass all but 50 μA of current at full scale, as you can verify by repeating the above calculation for each one.

Resistance Measurement

To measure a resistance the AMT must furnish a current, since a resistance does not have one of its own. It can then measure the current flowing through the resistance.

This section of the AMT consists in essence of a reference voltage in series with a current meter and the resistance to be measured, as shown in Figure 2-8. The resistors with values 3.55, 35.6, 365 ohms, and 4.66 kilohms are current-shunt resistors similar to those in Figure 2-7. The resistors with values 7.65, 84.5, 845 ohms, and 425 kilohms are range-selecting resistors (when the X100K range is selected, an additional 30 volts are added to the reference to maintain the current). R_x is the "unknown" resistance, connected to the meter's input terminals. R_1 is a current-limiting resistor that prevents the current through the moving coil of the meter movement exceeding the value for full deflection when the input terminals are shorted together (zero resistance).

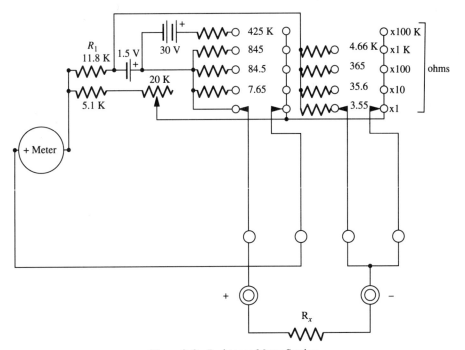

Figure 2-8   Resistance Meter Section

When this happens the AMT should read 0 ohms. The zero end of the scale is, therefore, at the right-hand end, as shown in Figure 2-9. When nothing is connected between the input terminals, no current flows, and the pointer stays at the left-hand end of the scale, indicating ∞ ohms, or "infinite resistance."

However, when a resistance is connected to the input, the meter pointer deflects in proportion to the current, which flows according to the total resistance in the circuit.

$$R_t = R_x + R_1 + R_m$$

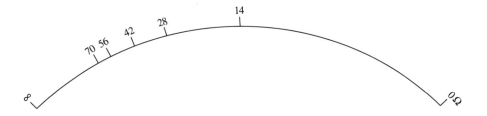

Figure 2-9   Resistance Scale

where R_t is the total resistance in the circuit, R_x the resistance being measured, R_1 the current-limiting resistor, and R_m the internal resistance of the meter.*

If the combined resistance of the meter and R_1 is 14 kilohms, and the reference voltage is a constant 1.5 V_{dc}, the current with the input shorted is 50 μA, which gives a full 90° deflection of the pointer. Increasing values of resistance connected to the input reduce the current, and consequently the deflection, as shown in Table 2-1.

TABLE 2-1   Reason for Nonlinearity of Ohms Scale

R_x (kilohms)	$(R_m + R_1)$ (kilohms)	R_t (kilohms)	I_t (μA)	Deflection (degrees)
0	14	14	50	90
14	14	28	25	45
28	14	42	16.7	30
42	14	56	12.5	23
56	14	70	10	18
70	14	84	8.3	15

This table shows why the ohms scale (Figure 2-9) is compressed toward the left-hand end. From 0 to 14 kilohms the pointer travels 45° for 14 kilohms, but from 56 to 70 kilohms only 3° for 14 kilohms. Consequently, only the right-hand part of the scale is really useful for precise measurement.

Since the measurement is made by passing the current from the battery through the resistance being measured, its accuracy is affected by the condition of the battery. As the battery ages, its current begins to fall off, so that the pointer no longer indicates 0 ohms when the input is shorted. This can be compensated for by the zero adjust potentiometer shown in Figure 2-8, which is connected in parallel with the meter and shunts some of the meter current. When the battery current is less than that necessary to give a 0 ohms reading with the input shorted, the ohms adjust control is reset to bypass less current,

---

*The value of R_m includes the value of its zero-adjust resistors. The zero-adjust resistance includes the potentiometer used to compensate for aging of the battery, as explained below.

so that the full 50-μA meter current is restored. This can only be done to a limited extent; the time will come when you cannot get the pointer to rest on the zero mark. The battery is then too old and must be replaced. A corollary to this is that *you must always zero the meter before taking a resistance reading* with the AMT, and this should be done for each range.

Decibel Measurement

The DB scale on an AMT is for measuring relative power levels. All decibel measurements are based on a reference power level. The most widely used reference is 1 milliwatt into a 600-ohm impedance. This is 0 dBm, and all values of dBm use this reference, which is the same as that used by values in volume units. You proceed as if you were making an ac voltage measurement, blocking dc if necessary, as explained previously. If your ac indication is on the 3-V range, you use the decibel value shown on the DB scale. If the ac indication is on a higher range, you use the dBm value shown on the DB scale plus the additional dBm value given for that range in the table printed on the AMT dial. The DB scale is made to track with the 3-V scale exactly, but it falls off by a factor of 1 dBm or more for values in the lower ⅓ of the scale on the higher ac ranges. The manufacturer's manual will supply a correction factor where required.

Continuity Testing

Continuity testing is a means of verifying that the connections in a circuit are as they should be. When using an AMT, you should use the lowest ohms range, since this gives the best resolution at low resistances. With the test probes applied to opposite ends of the conductor being checked, the reading should be 0 ohms (or close to it, if there is measurable resistance in the conductor). A reading of "infinity" indicates an open connection.

Some AMTs have a continuity sounder. These may have a separate range on the ohms function or a switch for continuity. When the continuity function is used, a buzzer sounds if there is not more than about 300 ohms resistance in the circuit being checked.

Test Leads

The test leads supplied with the AMT usually are a pair of flexible insulated wires. Their length varies, but usually falls in the range from 18 to 48 inches. Each lead is terminated with a banana plug or pin at one end and a simple probe (also called a test prod) at the other. The probe is for contacting the point where the measurement is to be made, and therefore, is made rigid and long enough to be held in your hand without your fingers contacting the circuit. At its end is a metal point for the actual contact. One lead and probe are colored red, the others black. The black lead is plugged into the AMT jack marked COM or $-$, the red lead into the other jack, or one of the other jacks, when there are more than one. Alligator clips with adapters to slip over the probe tips are available, and as mentioned above, one should be used on the black probe. Test probes that have a small hook on the end are also available. These are for attaching the probe to a wire or pin at the measurement point, and they are often preferred over alligator clips when working in a congested circuit (see Figure 2–10).

High-voltage probes are used for measuring the anode voltage in television sets, and other applications. These consist of a long handle, inside which is a resistance that divides the high voltage down to a value that can be handled by one of the dc ranges of the AMT. For instance, if the high voltage were 35 kilovolts, and a probe with the range 0–50 kV was used, you would select the 600 DC VOLTS range. You would then multiply by 100 the value of 350 V_{dc} indicated by the pointer to get the value of the high voltage.

Although not a probe in the sense described above, a clamp-on ammeter accessory can be used with some AMTs. This is used when the AMT does not have the capability of measuring the larger ac currents in 120-V_{ac} circuits. The clamp-on ammeter, shown schematically in Figure 2–11, has a pair of iron jaws that are opened for positioning around a current-carrying conductor, and then closed to complete a magnetic circuit. This allows the magnetic flux picked up from the conductor to induce a current in the secondary of a transformer in the adapter (the conductor being measured is the one-turn primary), and this current is then applied to one of the AC VOLTS ranges (where it develops a voltage across the range resistor), but is read as an ac current.

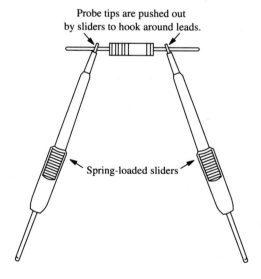

Probe tips are pushed out by sliders to hook around leads.

Spring-loaded sliders

Figure 2–10   Using Hook Probes

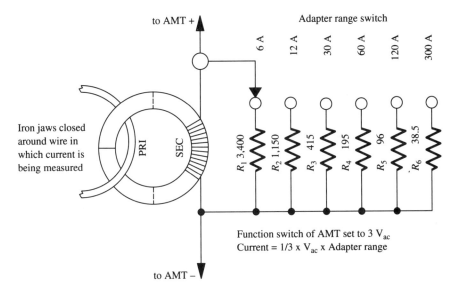

Figure 2–11   Clamp-on Meter Accessory

Zeroing the Pointer

When the pointer is at rest at the left-hand end of the scale, it should be over the zero mark on the voltage scales (ignore the ohms and dB scales). You should check this automatically when you go to use the AMT. Occasionally it is not at the zero mark, and you should then reset it to zero by means of the small plastic screw just below the dial. The correct way to do this is to rotate the screw with a small screwdriver until the pointer is to the right of the zero mark. Continue rotating the screw until the pointer returns to the zero position. The pointer should not be brought to the zero position from the left of the mark. Tap the glass *lightly* while doing this to eliminate friction error.

Adjusting the Ohms Function

You have already seen that the ohms section of the AMT has an adjustment for setting the pointer to the zero position on the ohms scale, which is at the right-hand end of that scale. This should be done every time you make a resistance measurement. After selecting the range, short the test leads together and set the pointer to 0 ohms by rotating the ohms adjust control. If the pointer cannot be zeroed, the battery is weak and must be replaced. Resistance values found with a weak battery cannot be accurate.

Reading the Meter Scale

Most AMTs have a *mirror scale,* in which you can see the pointer's reflected image. Always keep the pointer in line with its image when taking a reading to avoid *parallax error,* which is what happens when your eye is not directly above the pointer.

You have seen already that if you are not sure of the value of the voltage or current you are measuring you should start with the highest range, and switch downward to the best range. The best range is the one that puts the pointer on the upper part of the scale.

The principal divisions on the scale are numbered with two or three sets of numbers corresponding to the ranges, so begin by making sure you have the right one. Count the unnumbered increments carefully from the next lower numbered division. If the pointer stops in the space between the marks, estimate the additional increment as closely as you can. For example, in Figure 2–12 the pointer is resting between the two minor divisions that represent 2.3 and 2.4. You can estimate the value of the unmarked increment by mentally dividing the space into halves, and halves of halves, as shown in the inset. Since the pointer is slightly to the right of the first fourth of the minor subdivision, you would estimate this reading to be 2.33.

When measuring ac with some dc present, you should block the dc by connecting a 0.1-μF capacitor in series with the AMT input.

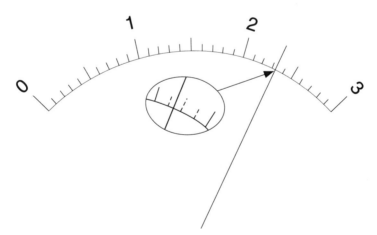

Figure 2–12   Reading the Meter

3

THE USER-FRIENDLY
DIGITAL MULTIMETER

The AMT operates by applying a current to an electromechanical device, the PMMC meter movement, that rotates accordingly. The pointer gives an indication in proportion to the strength of the current. Therefore, it is called an *analog* device.

The DMM in Figure 3-1 operates by converting the strength of the current into a numerical expression, and displaying that as a decimal number. There are none of the characteristic errors that are found in the AMT. Nor does

Figure 3-1 Digital Multimeter (DMM)

the user have to allow for his own possible mistakes, such as parallax error, range error, polarity error, and so on. This is not to say the DMM is foolproof; but it is much more *user-friendly,* a term used to describe some computers.

Like most computers, it is a *digital* device. It converts the incoming analog values of voltage, current, or resistance into digital expressions, which are then handled by digital circuits.

ANALOG-TO-DIGITAL CONVERSION

In a DMM a dual-slope analog-to-digital converter is used to convert the analog voltage being measured to a binary number. Figure 3-2 is a block diagram of one.

When an analog voltage to be measured is applied to the input, the following sequence of events takes place.

1. The analog voltage appears on the inverting input of the op-amp integrator.
2. A negative-going ramp appears at its output.
3. This negative-going ramp is applied to the inverting input of the op-amp comparator.
4. When this ramp goes a few microvolts below ground, the comparator switches, and its output goes high.
5. This places a high on one of the inputs of the AND gate, so that it can now pass positive-going clock signals.
6. These are counted by the counter until a designed total has been reached, at which point the control circuitry causes the input switch to select the negative reference voltage instead of the analog input voltage.
7. Now the output of the integrator ramps positive, but it has to start from the negative level it had reached when the switch changed over.
8. When the positive-going ramp crosses 0 volts, the comparator output switches low.
9. This places a low on the AND gate input to which it is connected, so the gate can no longer pass clock pulses.
10. The number of pulses that were required for the analog input voltage are displayed as a voltage reading.

In the inset of Figure 3-2, the two ramps are shown. The ramp due to the analog input is noisy, but the one due to the reference voltage is smooth. This is one of the advantages of the dual-slope ADC, since it gives a steadier reading.

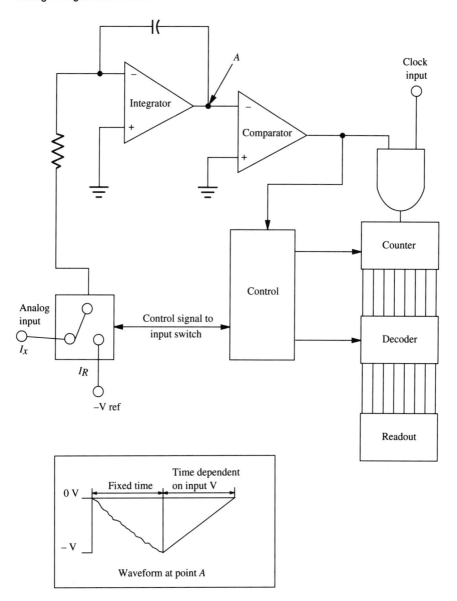

Figure 3-2   Dual-slope Analog-to-Digital Converter

Integrated circuits specifically designed for DMMs are produced by a number of manufacturers. These contain the circuits shown in Figure 3–2, plus others for autoranging, range hold, zero adjust, continuity, and so on. A typical IC is shown in Figure 3–3.

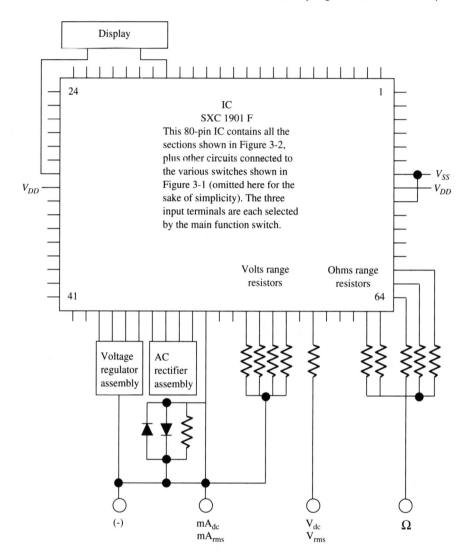

Figure 3–3   DMM Block Diagram

DMM CHARACTERISTICS

Digital Display

Most DMMs have a 3½-digit display, as shown in Figure 3–4 (a). This means that the first three digits from the right can each be any of the ten decimal (0–9) digits. The fourth (left-hand) digit can be a 1 only. Consequently, this display can show up to a maximum of 1999. A decimal point may be indicated between any two figures, so that the minimum display (other than zero) would be .001. Some DMMs have what is called a 3¾-digit display, in which the left-hand digit can be 1, 2, or 3, to show a maximum of 3999. The display gives other information also, the most important being function and unit.

Figure 3–4 (a)   3½-Digit Display

The decimal figures in the display are each made up of seven segments, as shown in Figure 3–4 (b). Each segment is connected to the output of a BCD-to-7-segment-decoder subsection of the IC. The decoder accepts information in binary form and converts it into seven outputs for connection to the seven-segment display. The decoder has what is called "ripple blanking." This causes the figures in the display to be turned on and off in sequence, so that they are energized one at a time (the others being off). This reduces the total power requirements, so the battery lasts longer. The ripple-blanking rate is such that the eye does not perceive any flicker.

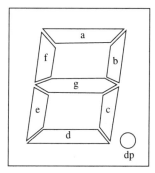

Figure 3–4 (b)   7-Segment Display

In most DMMs the display is a liquid crystal display (LCD). As shown in Figure 3–5, there are layers that create this effect. Light normally passes through the polarizers in both directions, and is reflected back to the viewer without interruption. When a voltage from the decoder is applied to a segment, a field is created between that segment and the substrate that causes the molecules in the liquid crystal material to turn and block the light, so that the segment appears black. Typically, the voltage applied to each segment is a square wave of 5 V_{pk} at 30 to 100 hertz.

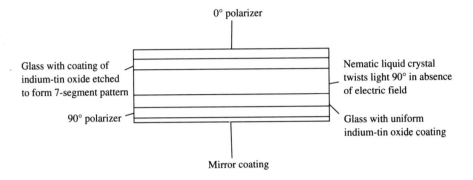

Figure 3–5 Principle of LCD

Accuracy

As mentioned before, the overall accuracy is derived from the individual accuracies of the reference voltage, the clock, and the counter. To these we should also add the accuracy of the range resistors in the input attenuator. As you can see in Figure 3–3, the range resistors are external to the IC, and must have sufficient accuracy to apply the precise degree of attenuation to the input. The reference voltage is supplied by the battery and regulated. If the battery needs to be replaced, the display shows BAT, BATT, or some similar indication.

DMM APPLICATIONS

Voltage Measurement

When using your DMM for voltage measurements, do not exceed the maximum input limits marked beside the input terminals. These are generally 1,000 V_{dc} or 500 V_{rms}. Use the test leads supplied with the unit, and take the same precautions given in Chapter 1 for avoiding injury to yourself or damage to the equipment. Set the function switch to DC V or AC V, as the case may be, and connect the probe to the point in the circuit where the voltage is to be read. Most DMMs have autoranging, so that the correct attenuation is applied automatically, and you can determine the range by the position of the decimal point. However, watch for the appearance in the display of "mV" if the voltage is a low one.

Although the DMM selects the range automatically, you may want to keep it on a specific range (for a series of measurements, or to avoid switching near the limits of a range). Most DMMs have a *range hold* switch or push button for this, and the DMM will stay on the range selected until it is released.

Another feature found in many DMMs is a *bar graph* on the display, beneath the numerical read-out. The regular display reads the rms value of an ac voltage, but the bar graph can show what it is peaking at.

Many DMMs have another feature called *data hold*. When you press the push button to activate this function, the DMM "freezes" the display at the value shown on it at that moment. This is a useful function for occasions when you cannot easily see the data while you are probing in a circuit.

The DMM does not mind if you connect the red lead to a negative voltage. It just shows a minus sign in front of the value. This feature is called *autopolarity*.

Resistance Measurements

Resistance measurements are made by passing a known value of constant current through the resistance being measured, and then measuring the voltage developed across it. If the resistance being measured is in a circuit, be sure and remove all power from the circuit, and ensure that all capacitors are fully discharged.

After turning the function switch to the ohms setting, connect the DMM probes across the resistance. The reading will probably be in kilohms, so no units will be displayed. However, on low values of resistance (usually 200 ohms and below) the ohms sign will appear. If the resistance is very high (over a megohm) the reading may take a few seconds to stabilize.

When measuring a low resistance, there may be some internal resistance (up to about 2 ohms) in the DMM that you should take into account. You can ascertain what this is by shorting the probe tips together. Then you can subtract it from the reading you get when you measure the resistance, or you can zero the meter by using the *zero adjust* function, where it is provided.

As the DMM sends a current through the resistance being measured, you need to know the strength of that current, so that you will not damage any sensitive component. This information is given in the manufacturer's manual. Typically, the voltage at the input jacks when nothing is connected to them is 1.5 or 2.0 V_{dc} on the lowest range, and 0.6 or 0.65 V_{dc} on the higher ranges.

If you accidentally connect the input to a voltage source when the DMM is in the ohms function, the fuse in series with the input lead may blow to protect the internal circuitry. If this happens, the display will indicate an open circuit. To verify if this is the case, short the input leads together. The reading will go to 000 if the fuse has not blown, but will continue to indicate an open circuit if it has. The indication for an open circuit is typically 1000, with a blinking 1.

Diode Check

All DMMs have a *diode check* function. In this function, a voltage of 1.5 or 2.0 V_{dc} is applied across the input jacks. A good silicon diode will conduct when forward biased with anything over 0.7 V_{dc}, so the display will show some value. If the diode is connected in the reverse direction, the indication for an open circuit will be displayed. However, if the diode is shorted the indication will be zero, or some very small resistance, in both directions.

Although the DMM can check silicon and germanium diodes, it cannot check light emitting diodes (LEDs). This is because they require a higher voltage than the DMM can supply.

Current Measurements

To measure the current at some point in a circuit, you have to break the circuit and connect the test leads across the gap. You should begin, therefore, by removing power from the circuit. Then set the function switch to DC mA or AC mA (but some DMMs do not have separate switch positions for dc and ac current). Connect the test leads to the opposite sides of the break in the circuit, so that the circuit current will flow through the DMM when the power is restored. Turn the power back on.

Accidental contact with a voltage source (or if the current exceeds the maximum allowable value) will probably cause the input fuse to blow, in which case you will get no reading.

Continuity Tests

Most DMMs have a continuity test function. When you select this, an internal buzzer will sound if resistance of 300 ohms or less exists in the part of the circuit between the points where the test leads are applied. This function allows you to concentrate on the circuit, so you don't have to watch the read-out.

Replacement of Battery or Fuse

As mentioned previously, an indication will appear in the display to notify you if the battery requires replacing. The battery, and the method of replacing it, will vary with different instruments. The details will be given in the manufacturer's manual. But before removing the battery compartment cover, turn off the power and unplug the test leads. *Do not operate the DMM with the cover removed.*

Similarly, when replacing the fuse, be sure to use the proper value. Most DMMs use a miniature 0.315-A fuse (an instrument fuse), which can be obtained from any electronic parts store. Again, *do not operate the DMM without the fuse compartment cover.*

USING THE DMM

Safety Precautions

A DMM is no less hazardous than an AMT if not used with care. In using it, you must always be conscious of possible hazards to yourself and to the instrument. No apology is made for reminding you of the safety precautions given in Chapter 1.

Test Leads

The same types of test leads are used by the DMM as are used by the AMT (see Chapter 2). The big difference between the inputs of the two instruments is in the input impedance. The AMT, as you saw in the previous chapter, has a comparatively low input impedance, but the DMM has an impedance of 10 megohms. This has a negligible effect on the circuit in which a measurement is being made, so that it is much more suitable for use in semiconductor circuits, where the AMT would have a loading effect.

Zero Adjust

The only zero adjust is that described previously, under resistance measurements.

Autorange and Range Hold

These features are not found in AMTs. The autorange feature is one that automatically selects the proper attenuation to adjust the input voltage to fall within the range of the reference voltage. It is provided in the DMM IC. This is a very useful function. It prevents you from applying an input that is above or below the correct range, and saves time in taking a reading. When making several measurements, it is helpful to have the range changed automatically as you move the probe from point to point.

However, there are times when you don't want this to happen, so the range hold function is provided to override the autorange function. This locks in the range in use, so that it will not change if a measurement results in a reading outside its limits. It has to be released before the autorange resumes control.

Microvolt Measurements

While DMMs have a range for millivolts, they do not have one for microvolts. If you have a need for this capability, you can provide it by building the circuit shown in Figure 3-6. This can be done on a perfboard mounted in

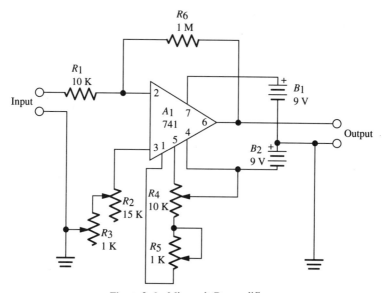

Figure 3-6   Microvolt Preamplifier

a small box, with input test leads and output leads that plug into the DMM input. There are very few parts, and they are readily available at any electronics parts store (such as Radio Shack). You will need the following.

A_1	741 operational amplifier
B_1	9-V battery
B_2	9-V battery
R_1	10-kΩ ±5% fixed resistor
R_2	15-kΩ potentiometer
R_3	1-kΩ potentiometer
R_4	10-kΩ potentiometer
R_5	1-kΩ potentiometer
R_6	1-MΩ ±5% fixed resistor

Hardware, test leads, and so on, as required

Choose fixed resistors as close to their nominal values as possible, so that R_6 is as near as you can get to exactly 100 times R_1.

After assembling the circuit, you must calibrate it as follows.

Step 1: Connect the amplifier output to the DMM input.

Step 2: Set DMM to read dc volts (or millivolts, if it does not have autorange).

Step 3: Apply power to DMM and amplifier.
Step 4: Short together the amplifier input test leads.
Step 5: Adjust R_2 to about 10 kΩ.
Step 6: Adjust R_4 for a zero reading on the DMM.
Step 7: If you cannot get an exact zero on the DMM by adjusting R_4, readjust R_2.
Step 8: If necessary, adjust R_3 and R_5 for more exact results.

Since this amplifier has a gain of 100, an input voltage of 10 μV is going to become an output of 1 mV. Therefore, the millivolt readings on the DMM are produced by amplifier input voltages which have the following values.

Reading on DMM (mV)	Value in Microvolts (μV)
1	10
10	100
100	1,000

TROUBLESHOOTING
WITH MULTIMETERS

The greatest use of AMTs and DMMs is in troubleshooting circuits and components. Determining voltages and currents in circuits, and continuity and resistance of circuits and components are what they do best.

RESISTANCE

There are two kinds of resistance: static and dynamic. Static resistance is that of a component or circuit in which no current or voltage is present, and it can be measured with the ohms function of an AMT or a DMM. Dynamic resistance is that which is present when the circuit is active, and it cannot be measured with the ohms function. You need to measure voltage or current. To illustrate the difference, consider a 100-watt light bulb. With a DMM you can measure the resistance of its filament, which comes to about 10.7 ohms. This is its resistance *cold*. But when you put the bulb in its socket, and switch on the 120-V_{rms} current, you cannot measure its internal resistance. You can only arrive at it by measuring the actual voltage of the house current and using Ohm's Law. The current is given by

$$I = P/V = 100/120 = 0.833 \text{ A}.$$

Then its dynamic resistance is given by

$$R = P/I^2 = 100/0.694 = 144 \ \Omega.$$

We shall begin with static resistance measurements.

Static Resistance Measurements

Continuity.   Continuity testing is something that is done to verify whether a continuous current path exists between two points. Many DMMs and some AMTs have sounders that buzz if the resistance is, say, 300 ohms or less between the points where the probes are applied. This is very convenient, because you don't have to look at the meter, and you can concentrate on the circuit.

However, this procedure should be used with caution. There are some conditions that can give a continuity indication even though there is a problem. An example would be a cold solder joint. This is a connection where the solderer did not get all the solder properly melted and in contact with all parts of the joint. There is a low-resistance contact, which is below the level that would prevent the sounder from buzzing, but it can cause problems in the circuit nonetheless. Other examples are internal shorts in components that only happen when high voltage is applied. However, on the whole, continuity testing is a very useful troubleshooting technique, especially on printed circuit boards.

Resistance.   In measuring resistance, it is well to consider the effects of temperature. The resistance of metals increases with temperature rise (as you saw with the light bulb). On the other hand, the resistance of semiconductors decreases. A thermistor is a temperature-sensitive device, whose resistance decreases as the temperature goes up. Placed in series with a battery and a current meter, it turns the current meter into a thermometer. This property of substances to change their resistance according to the temperature is called their *temperature coefficient.* If the resistance rises with temperature, it is *positive;* if it goes down, it is *negative.*

Ordinary fixed resistors are neither metal nor semiconductor, and their temperature coefficient is seldom of any concern. Their values are marked on them with colored bands, as shown in Table 4-1.

These bands are grouped on the resistor body, as shown in Figure 4-1, closer to one end than to the other, and they are read from the nearer end. The first two bands are the significant figures, the third is the multiplier, and the fourth the tolerance. There is usually no fourth band on a ± 20 percent resistor.

Measuring the value of a resistor that is not in a circuit is easy. The AMT or DMM probes are applied to the resistor's two leads, and the value read. On

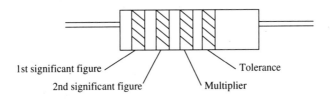

1st significant figure

2nd significant figure

Tolerance

Multiplier

Figure 4-1   Color Coding on Resistor

TABLE 4–1   Resistor Color Codes

Color	Significant Figures	Multiplier	Tolerance
Black	0	1	±20%
Brown	1	10	±1%
Red	2	100	±2%
Orange	3	1,000	±3%
Yellow	4	10,000	±4%
Green	5	100,000	
Blue	6	1,000,000	
Violet	7	10,000,000	
Gray	8	100,000,000	
White	9		
Gold		0.1	±5%
Silver		0.01	±10%
No color			±20%

the AMT you have to set the range, which is usually the one that gives the best resolution. You don't have to do this on the DMM, unless it does not have autorange.

In-Circuit Resistance.   Service data for television receivers and similar equipment usually provide resistance values from various points in the circuit to ground. These can be measured with the ohms function of a DMM or AMT, with the power off in the circuit.

Unless stated otherwise, the tolerance for such values is ±20 percent. When a value is found that is outside the limits, you should look for the possibility of defective diodes or transistors, resistors that have changed value (often as a result of overheating, which should also be investigated), or shorted or leaky capacitors.

Very High Resistance.   An AMT such as the one in Figure 2–1 can measure resistance up to about 100 megohms, but the poor resolution of the left-hand end of the scale makes it impossible to get an accurate reading. However, you can do better with the DMM.

With the DMM, the resistance to be measured and a 9-volt battery, connected as in Figure 4–2, measure the dc voltages at V_1 and V_2. Then substitute these values into the following equation.

$$R_x = 10\frac{(V_1 - V_2)}{V_2}$$

R_x will be in megohms. For example, if $V_1 = 9$ V_{dc}, and the DMM reads V_2 as 150 mV, then R_x is given by

$$R_x = 10\,\frac{(9 - 0.15)}{0.15} = 590\text{ M}\Omega.$$

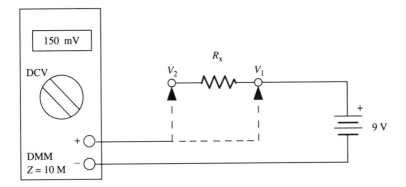

Figure 4-2 Using the DMM to Measure Very High Resistances

Attenuator Pads. To measure the input resistance of an attenuator pad with the DMM ohms function, connect a resistor with the same value as the pad's normal load to its output. Then measure the input resistance of the pad, which should be the pad's normal impedance. For instance, a 75-ohm pad intended for use between two 75-ohm lines, connected in this way, should measure 75 ohms.

Internal Resistance of PMMC Meter Movement. If you try to measure the internal resistance of the movement of an analog meter directly, you will probably burn it out. In an AMT the maximum current that it will take is 50 μA. If you use another AMT in the ohms function, the current from that AMT's battery is almost certain to be too much for the movement being measured.

However, this measurement can be performed safely if the circuit shown in Figure 4-3 is used. Potentiometer R_1 is adjusted to give a full-scale deflection of the meter pointer. Then potentiometer R_2 is connected and adjusted until the meter pointer reads exactly half the first value. This potentiometer is then disconnected without changing its setting, and its resistance is measured. This will be the internal resistance of the meter movement.

Tracing Short Circuits on PC Boards. When there is no voltage at the collector of a transistor, for instance, the DMM may show 0 volts, but using the DMM preamplifier described in the previous chapter, you can often find that there is a small voltage.

The procedure for localizing the short is to probe with the red lead along the conductor from the collector toward the output terminal. The black lead is connected to ground. At the point where the short circuit exists, the DMM

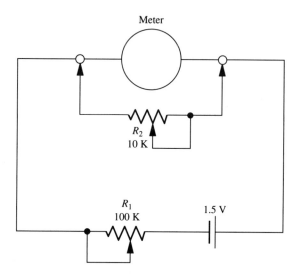

Caution: Each potentiometer must be set to maximum before applying power.

Figure 4-3   Measuring Internal Resistance of PMMC Meter Movement

reading should increase. For instance, if at first it was 100 μV, after passing the point where the short is, it might increase to 200 μV. A careful search around this point should be carried out to find the short.

In the same way, a short between a conductor and V_{cc} will cause a power supply potential to exist all along its length. The preamplifier's red lead is connected to V_{cc}, and the black lead probes along the conductor. The minute change of voltage in the vicinity of the short will be detected as before.

If the voltage decreases (or increases) all along the conductor, you would assume that the problem was at the end (perhaps inside an IC).

Diodes.   Diodes (see Figure 4-4) are tested by using the ohms function of your AMT or DMM, or the diode check function of your DMM.

In the diode check function of the DMM, a typical voltage of 1.5 V_{dc} is present between the input jacks. Connect the DMM test leads to opposite ends of the diode. (You need to know which lead is positive and which is negative; usually the red one is positive.) However, you may not know for sure which end of the diode is the cathode and which is the anode (see Figure 4-4). If the diode is good, the DMM will read either some low value of ohms, or a very high one (possibly it will indicate overrange). Reverse the connections, so that the red and black leads are now at the opposite ends of the diode. If the low reading becomes a high one, or the high reading becomes a low one, the diode is definitely good. If there is no change, a low reading both ways indicates a shorted diode, and a high reading both ways indicates an open diode.

You can do the same test with an AMT's ohms function. However, the AMT does not have a special voltage for checking diodes, so you must choose

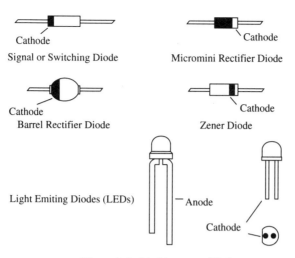

Figure 4-4 Markings on a Diode

the range according to what the voltage will be. The X10 range is generally used to avoid exceeding the diode current rating, but in some cases you may have to use the X1 range to get enough voltage for forward bias.

Light emitting diodes (LEDs) are different from silicon and germanium diodes. An LED generally has a forward resistance of about 20 kilohms and a very high reverse resistance. Most DMMs cannot test LEDs with the diode check function, and AMTs do not do much better. Other methods of testing are described on page [69].

Silicon Controlled Rectifiers (SCRs).   These can be tested using the ohms function of a DMM. The DMM red lead is connected to terminal 1 (the anode) and to terminal 2 (the cathode) of the SCR, leaving the gate open. The DMM should read a very high resistance. Reverse the connections of the leads, and a similar high reading should be obtained. Reconnect the leads the way they were at first, and then short the gate lead to the anode lead. The DMM reading will drop to a low resistance value.

Remove the short, but do not change the other connections. There should be no change in the reading. Disconnect, then reconnect the DMM leads, and the previous high resistance reading will return. These responses indicate a good SCR.

Bipolar Junction Transistors (BJTs).   Since a BJT has two junctions, it is the same as two diodes connected back-to-back. One diode is between the collector and base leads, the other is between the emitter and base leads. You can test these "diodes" in the same way as other diodes, with a DMM or AMT. Each should read a high resistance in one direction, a low resistance in the other. Then connect the DMM or AMT between the collector and emitter. You should get a high resistance reading either way.

You can also test BJTs in circuit, using a voltage method described below, or by an oscilloscope method described in Chapter 7. (See Figure 4–5 for different transistor types.)

Junction Field-Effect Transistors (JFETs).   JFETs must be handled with care, because they are very susceptible to damage from static charges

Plastic Case: pins in straight line (TO92)

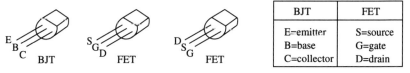

BJT	FET
E=emitter	S=source
B=base	G=gate
C=collector	D=drain

Plastic Case: pins in semicircle

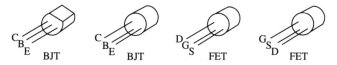

Metal Case: pins in semicircle (TO39)

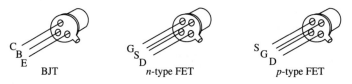

Metal Case: case is collector (TO3)

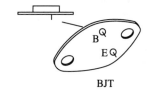

Plastiac Case: metal heat sink (TO220)

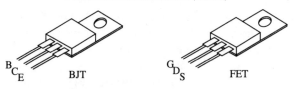

Figure 4–5   Various Transistor Types

(which you may carry on your body). Their leads should be inserted in conductive foam, twisted around each other, or wrapped in metal foil, except when mounted in a circuit.

To test one, connect the leads of an AMT or DMM in the ohms function between the source and drain. You should measure resistance anywhere between 100 ohms and 10 kilohms. Reversing the connections of the leads should give the same reading.

Then connect the test leads between the gate and source. In the case of an N-channel JFET, connect the negative lead to the source. There should be a low resistance reading. In the case of a P-channel JFET, the reading should be very high. Then reverse the connections; the readings should be the opposite of what they were before. Repeat this step for the gate and drain.

Now connect the test leads between the drain and source. The reading will be either very high or low, depending upon the type of JFET and the polarity of the test leads. Reverse the connections to get opposite results.

Metal-Oxide Semiconductor FET (MOSFET).   The same precautions should be taken in handling a MOSFET as a JFET (see above). However, use a DMM for testing a MOSFET. Begin by connecting a 1-megohm resistor between the gate and the source of the MOSFET. Then connect another 1-megohm resistor to the gate, but do not connect the other end to anything yet.

Now connect the DMM test leads to the source and drain. If the MOSFET is a P-channel device, connect the negative lead to the drain. Do it the other way around if it's an N-channel device. The DMM resistance reading should be anywhere from 100 ohms to 10 kilohms for a depletion device, but an enhancement device will give an infinite resistance reading.

With the test leads still connected as before, short the open end of the second 1-megohm resistor to the drain. The resistance reading on the DMM should drop to a lower value. Do this several times. If the MOSFET is good, the drop should be quite large.

Triacs.   Most triacs can be tested in the following way. If the one you have is a particularly sensitive triac, use a low-value resistor in series with the DMM's red test lead. On the other hand, if you have a triac that cannot respond to the voltage between the DMM test leads, you cannot test it by this method.

Begin by connecting the red test lead to main terminal 1 and the black lead to main terminal 2. The DMM should display a very high resistance value.

Now short the gate momentarily to main terminal 1. The DMM reading will drop to a much lower value. Remove the short. The reading should remain unaltered.

Disconnect the test leads, and then reconnect them, but with the red lead to main terminal 2. The DMM should read a very high resistance again. Now short the gate to main terminal 2. The DMM reading should drop to a low value. Remove the short; there should be no change in the reading. Remove the test leads, and then reconnect them. The DMM should read the former high resistance value.

Dynamic Resistance

As stated earlier, dynamic resistance is resistance measured with the power on, so that it cannot be measured with the ohms function of the AMT or DMM. To show how this is done, look at Figure 4–6. Here, you want to measure the dynamic resistance between point A and ground.

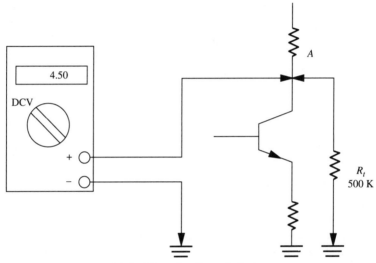

Figure 4-6 Measuring Dynamic Resistance

First connect the DMM in the dc volts function between point A and ground, and note the voltage reading. Then disconnect the DMM, and connect a high-value resistor (say, 500 kilohms) between point A and ground. Then measure the voltage between A and ground again. The unknown resistance R_x is given by

$$R_x = R_t \frac{(V_1 - V_2)}{V_2}$$

where R_t is the test resistor value in ohms, V_1 the original voltage reading without the test resistor, and V_2 the second voltage reading after connecting the test resistor.

For example, if $V_1 = 5.0$ V$_{dc}$, $V_2 = 4.5$ V$_{dc}$, and $R_t = 500$ kΩ, then

$$R_x = 500 \times 10^3 \frac{(5.0 - 4.5)}{4.5}$$

$$= 55{,}556 \ \Omega.$$

VOLTAGE

Books on electronics stress that the DMM is the better instrument for measuring voltages in modern electronic circuits, because it has a much higher input impedance than the AMT. There are some situations in which an AMT voltage reading can be off more than 90 percent, although the error is usually much less than that.

As an example, suppose you want to measure the bias voltage on the base of the transistor in the circuit shown in Figure 4-7. A simple Ohm's Law calculation tells you that the voltage should be 0.64 V_{dc}. If you were to use a 2,000 ohms per volt AMT on its lowest range of 0–10 V_{dc}, you should be using an instrument with an input impedance of 20 kilohms on that range. That is to say, you would be shunting R_2 with a resistance of 20 kilohms. The combined value of the AMT's input impedance and R_2 would then be 6.67 kilohms. The voltage dropped across R_2 would now be only 0.47 V_{dc}, which would not only be inaccurate, but would cause a silicon transistor to cease conducting. But this is not all. You would be making this reading near the left-hand end of the scale where the accuracy is less, and as this AMT has an accuracy of ±3 percent of full scale, the real value could be anywhere between 0.17 and 0.77 V_{dc}. Obviously, this is not very precise.

The situation is somewhat better with a 20,000 ohms per volt AMT. Its shunting effect makes the reading on the 0–3 V range 0.56 V_{dc} (which would cause the transistor to cease conducting also). However, this AMT has an accuracy on dc ranges of ±1½ percent of full scale (3 V), so the uncertainty of the reading now is 0.56 ±(3 × 0.015) V, or anywhere between 0.515 and 0.605 V_{dc}. Here again, however, you have to read this at the left-hand end of the scale where the accuracy is less.

The DMM with its input impedance of 10 megohms places a negligible load on the circuit. Its shunting effect changes the value of R_2 by only 10 ohms, and it reads the value of the voltage as 0.64 ±0.0064 V_{dc}, assuming a ±1 percent tolerance. It certainly will not affect the operation of the transistor.

However, the dc resistance is only part of the impedance. A DMM has a capacitance paralleling its input resistance. This is usually less than 100 pF, but still enough to interfere with the operation of a high-frequency radio or TV circuit, especially the local oscillator.

To avoid this problem, you can use a low-capacitance probe with the DMM. Such a probe will have a capacitive impedance of 1 pF or less. It also has a precise attenuation factor (X1, X10, or X100), but a much lower resistive impedance than the DMM.

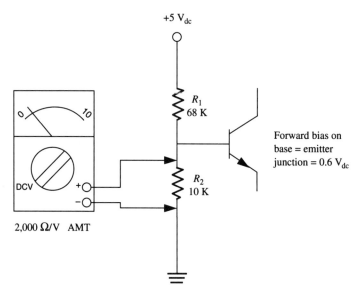

Figure 4-7   Circuit Loading by an AMT

However, if you do not have such a probe, you can use a 100-kilohm resistor in series with the regular probe. This will isolate the DMM's input capacitance from the circuit, but it will have an effect on the reading. To get the true dc volts reading, you will have to multiply the actual reading by 1.01. This does not make very much difference in practice and is usually ignored.

If the voltage is not being measured with respect to ground, it will be necessary to use an isolation resistor in series with both probes if capacitive effects are to be avoided. Some other probes will be described later.

DC Voltage Measurements

BJT Testing In Circuit.   To test a BJT while it is operating in a circuit, (1) connect your DMM across the collector load resistor (as shown in Figure 4-8) with the red lead connected to the collector end of the resistor. If the reading is positive, the transistor is *pnp*. If it is negative, *npn*. In the latter case, reverse the DMM test leads for a positive reading.

Now short the emitter to the base. If the transistor is working properly, the DMM reading should decrease. No change indicates a problem in the collector-emitter circuit.

(2) Remove the DMM test leads from the load resistor and the base-emitter short, and measure the bias voltage between the emitter and the base. If it is low, or nonexistent, connect the test leads between the collector and ground. Note the reading. Then connect a 10-kilohm resistor between the collector and the base. The collector voltage should decrease, because the

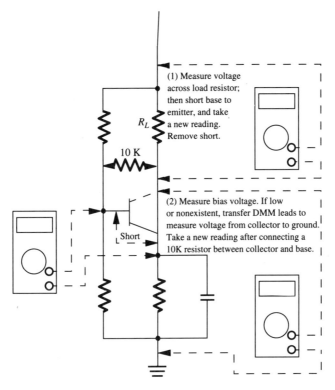

Figure 4-8   BJT Testing in Common-Emitter Circuit

increased bias should result in increased collector current. If nothing happens, you need to check the bias circuit.

Pulse Measurements.   You can measure pulse amplitude and width with the dc volts function of a DMM (within its frequency capability, of course). It is necessary for the pulse train to have positive excursions only—no negative. If it does have negative as well as positive excursions, it can be converted into a dc pulse train with a clamp, as shown in Figure 4-9.

With a dc pulse train, connect the DMM to read its voltage. This will be the *average* voltage of the train, as shown in Figure 4-10. To measure the *peak* value, you need the peak hold probe shown in Figure 4-11, unless the DMM has a peak hold function (some do). You also need to know the pulse period (P_p). The pulse width P_w is given by

$$P_w = \frac{P_p \times V_{\text{avg}}}{V_{pk}}.$$

Zener Diode In-Circuit Test.   As long as a zener diode is within its operating range, the voltage across it remains constant, no matter what the

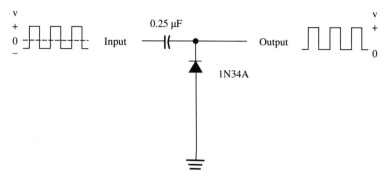

Figure 4–9   Removing Negative Excursions with a Clamp

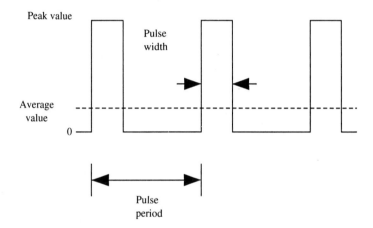

Figure 4–10   Measuring Pulse Peak and Average Values for Pulse Width

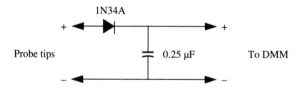

Figure 4–11   Peak Hold Probe

current. This characteristic enables you to test a zener diode without removing it from the circuit.

If, when you measure the dc voltage across the load paralleling the diode, you find it is below the value it should be, you may suspect the diode of leakage. To verify this, disconnect one end of the diode. If the diode is leaking, the voltage across the load will increase sharply. If there is no change, then the fault is not in the diode, but in an overload somewhere in the load circuit.

On the other hand, if the voltage across the load is higher than normal, the diode may be open. This will be confirmed if there is no change when one end of the zener diode is disconnected.

Zener Diode Out-of-Circuit Test.   This is a more accurate test than the in-circuit test just described. You need a voltage source that is a little higher than the zener diode's rated voltage. For most diodes a 9-volt battery will suffice.

Connect the zener diode in the circuit shown in Figure 4–12. The 3-kilohm potentiometer enables you to vary the applied voltage from zero up to 9 V_{dc}. The 1-kilohm current-limiting resistor protects the diode.

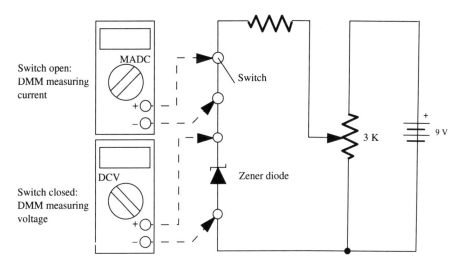

Figure 4–12   Zener Diode Test

The first step is to connect the DMM across the open switch with the potentiometer set to minimum. Set the DMM to read dc mA, and then slowly increase the voltage while watching the DMM. When the voltage reaches the diode's *breakdown voltage,* the current will increase rapidly and continue to increase with further voltage increase.

Now reset the DMM to read dc volts, and reconnect it across the zener diode; close the switch. Rotate the potentiometer in the opposite direction. The DMM reading should not change as long as the applied voltage does not go below the breakdown voltage.

Tunnel Diode.   Test a tunnel diode in a similar way to a zener diode. However, some tunnel diodes require several hundred volts to make them switch, so you need a bench power supply capable of delivering the necessary voltage.

Begin with the power supply adjusted for minimum output. Connect the tunnel diode in series with a current-limiting resistor across the power supply output. Connect the DMM, set to read dc volts, across the diode.

Increase the power supply output voltage slowly, while watching the DMM reading. It will be near zero at first, but when the diode switches it will jump up to about 0.5 V_{dc}. Note the power supply voltage at which this happens. Then reduce the power supply voltage slowly, until the DMM reading drops back to near zero. Note the power supply voltage again. The two voltages should agree. This indicates a good diode.

AC Voltage Measurements

In an AMT the ac voltage input impedance is usually much less than the dc input impedance. A 20,000 ohms per volt AMT will typically have an ac impedance of 5,000 ohms per volt. This makes the DMM the better instrument to use for many ac voltage measurements.

Waveform.   The actual DMM circuit measures rms voltage. Table 4–2 shows the factors to multiply the rms reading by to get peak, peak-to-peak, and average values. However, these are only true for sine waves. With any other waveform the DMM will lose all accuracy. If you are in doubt about whether the waveform you are measuring is a sine wave, you should view it on an oscilloscope to be sure.

TABLE 4–2   Sine Wave Conversion Factors

To Convert	To			
	Average	RMS	Peak	Peak-to-Peak
average	1.000	1.111	1.572	3.144
rms	0.899	1.000	1.414	2.828
peak	0.636	0.707	1.000	2.000
peak-to-peak	0.318	0.353	0.500	1.000

True RMS AC Voltmeter.   The true rms value of nonsinusoidal waveforms can be measured directly using a *true rms ac voltmeter.* It is not an instrument that will be used much in troubleshooting, however. Since nonsinusoidal waveforms can be displayed on an oscilloscope, it is no problem to measure their peak values, as explained in a later chapter. The rms value of a square wave is the same as its peak value; the rms value of a sawtooth wave is 0.577 times its peak value; the rms value of a half-rectified sine wave is half its peak value; and the rms value of a full-rectified sine wave is 0.707 times its peak value.

AC Waveforms with DC Components.   In many cases the voltage you want to measure consists of both ac and dc. If the dc component is greater than the peak value of the ac component, it is called pulsating dc. Otherwise it is called ac with a dc component. You can remove the dc component by connecting a capacitor in series with the DMM or AMT input, but it must have sufficient capacitance to pass the ac without attenuating it, and the ability to withstand the peak voltage.

Frequency Response.   The frequency response of multimeters is limited. For example, a typical DMM that has an accuracy of ± 1 percent of reading at 60 Hz will have an accuracy of only ± 6 percent at 10 kHz. This can be extended to 10 MHz, however, by using a peak reading probe, as shown in Figure 4–13. In this probe the germanium diode rectifies the ac signal so that it reaches the DMM as pulsating dc, and it is read as a dc voltage with the DMM in its dc volts mode. However, because of the forward bias required to make the diode conduct, the probe cannot respond to signals below 0.2 V_{dc}. (You could bias the diode with a bias box providing 0.2 V_{dc} and be able to read lower voltages, but the values would not be accurate.) This probe's frequency response can be extended to 200 MHz by adding a 100-kilohm resistor where shown, but the voltage values read by the DMM would then have to be multiplied by 1.01 for true values. (This would not be significant in most cases.) If you make such a probe, build it in a shielded enclosure of some kind, with a shielded lead connecting it to the DMM.

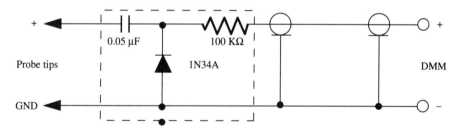

Figure 4–13   Peak Reading Probe for High Frequency

5

MORE SCOPE WITH THE SCOPE

If electronic measuring instruments were chess pieces, the oscilloscope would be the Queen, since it can perform many of the functions of the other pieces. However, the most widely used feature is its ability to make the invisible visible.

The shapes of invisible waveforms are made to appear on the screen of the cathode-ray tube (CRT), which is the heart of the oscilloscope. The CRT is a funnel-shaped sealed glass enclosure that contains a high vacuum. As shown in Figure 5-1, this tube is narrow at one end and broad at the other. The narrow end contains an assembly called an electron gun, which generates and projects a beam of electrons that impinges on a phosphor screen coating the inner surface of the other end. This screen glows where the electron beam strikes it. Between the electron gun and the phosphor screen are two pairs of metal plates that deflect the beam by means of the voltages applied to them, so that a representation of some function appears on the screen.

The Electron Gun

The electron gun is shown in more detail in Figure 5-2. A cup-shaped nickel *cathode* is coated with barium-calcium-strontium oxide, a substance that emits electrons copiously when heated. Inside the cathode is a twisted tungsten filament with aluminum-oxide insulation that heats the cathode when the CRT is energized.

Surrounding the cathode is a larger cup, also of nickel. It has an aperture in the end facing the screen. This electrode has a negative potential relative to the potential of the cathode. Its voltage is adjusted by a potentiometer called

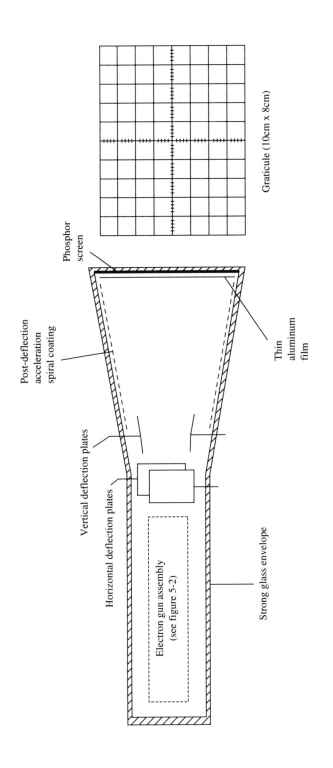

Graticule (10cm x 8cm)

Phosphor screen

Post-deflection acceleration spiral coating

Thin aluminum film

Vertical deflection plates

Horizontal deflection plates

Electron gun assembly (see figure 5-2)

Strong glass envelope

Figure 5–1 Cathode-ray Tube

57

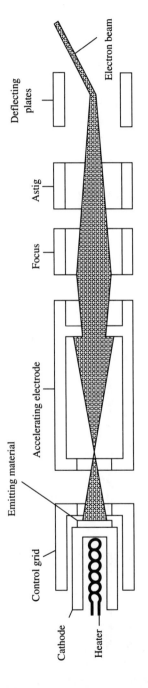

Typical Voltages

Cathode	-2,000 V$_{dc}$
Control grid	-2,015 V$_{dc}$
Accelerating electrode	0 V$_{dc}$
Focus	-500 V$_{dc}$
Astigmatism	+50 V$_{dc}$

Figure 5-2 Electron Gun

the *intensity control*. As it becomes more negative, it repels more of the cathode electrons, reducing the number that can escape through its aperture. Because its action is analogous to that of the grid in a vacuum tube, it is called the *control grid*.

Beyond the control grid is the *accelerating electrode*. This is a nickel cylinder with a positive potential with respect to the cathode. The negative voltage on the control grid has a pinching effect on the stream of electrons flowing from the cathode, They are drawn into the cylinder in a narrow beam and accelerated by its relatively positive voltage. The combined electrostatic field of both electrodes causes the electrons to converge and cross over within the accelerating electrode.

On emerging from the accelerating electrode, the electron beam passes through the *focus electrode,* where it is shaped into a long thin cone, with its apex on the phosphor screen. It then goes through the *astigmatism control,* which ensures that the beam has a circular cross section.

The Phosphor Screen

The screen on modern CRTs is rectangular, and it is formed by coating the inside of the glass with a crystalline substance called a phosphor. Most scopes use a phosphor that responds with a green fluorescence when the electron beam intensity is low, but glows blue as the intensity is increased.

A very thin film of aluminum is deposited on the inner surface of the phosphor. It is transparent to electrons, but not to light. The electron beam passes through it and excites the phosphor; but instead of half the light being wasted by shining into the interior of the CRT, it is reflected by the aluminum "mirror," and emerges from the front. This increases contrast as well as brightness, since the dark areas appear darker.

The inside of the screen face plate is marked with a *graticule*. This is a grid of vertical and horizontal lines that provides a scale for reading the parameters of the display, as shown in Figure 5-3. Vertical divisions measure amplitude, horizontal divisions measure time.

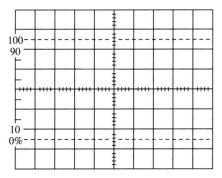

Figure 5-3   Graticule

The Deflection Plates

As mentioned above, the electron beam passes between the *deflection plates* as it travels from the electron gun to the phosphor screen. There are two pairs of these. One pair has its plates situated at the sides. These are used for deflecting the beam horizontally, so they are called the *horizontal deflection plates*.

The electron beam is swept from side to side by voltages on these plates, so that a horizontal line appears on the screen if there is no change in the voltages on the vertical deflection plates. At the beginning of each sweep there is a high positive voltage on the left-hand plate (as viewed from the screen end of the CRT) and a corresponding negative voltage on the right-hand plate. These voltages bend the electron beam as it passes between them, so that the beam impacts the left-hand side of the screen. The voltages on the plates decrease at a steady rate, bending the beam less and less, until it is not bent at all and is striking the middle of the screen. From then on the left-hand plate becomes steadily more negative and the right-hand plate becomes steadily more positive, until the beam has been bent to strike the screen at its right-hand edge.

At this point a strong negative voltage is applied to the control grid, cutting off the electron beam entirely, and the plate voltages revert to what they were at the start. The strong negative voltage is removed from the control grid so that the beam is restored, and it strikes the left-hand edge of the screen again.

At the slower sweep rates you see the point of impact of the beam move horizontally across the screen from left to right, vanish, reappear at the left, cross it again, and so on. You do not see it as it returns from right to left, because it has been cut off, or "blanked." At higher sweep rates you see only a straight horizontal line, because the sweep action is too fast for the eye to follow.

The *vertical deflection plates* are mounted above and below the electron beam. If a positive voltage is applied to the upper plate and a negative voltage to the lower plate, they bend the beam upward so that it impacts the screen at a higher point. If the voltages are reversed, the beam is moved downward into the lower part of the screen. If the vertical voltages rise and fall while the horizontal plates are moving the beam sideways, a wavy line will appear on the screen. This is how a waveform is displayed.

Secondary Emission

The beam electrons are called *primary electrons*. Where they strike the screen, energy is transferred from them to the electrons in the phosphor. Some of these acquire enough energy to escape by *secondary emission*. These secondary electrons are then attracted by the high potential on an adjacent aquadag coating on the inside of the CRT, thus completing the circuit. This potential, like that in a TV picture tube, is quite high relative to that on the cathode. (In the scope in Figure 5–4 the voltages between the anode and the cathode is 12.6 kV_{dc}.)

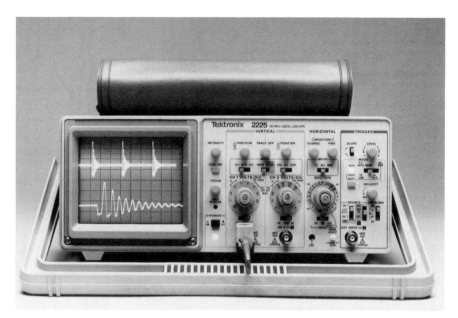

Figure 5-4 Typical Oscilloscope

In many modern CRTs there is a narrow ribbon of resistive material in the form of a helical spiral from near the deflection plates to the screen. This acts as a continuous voltage divider to the high voltage applied across this spiral, so that the electron beam experiences increasing acceleration as it approaches the screen. This is called *post-deflection acceleration*. A brighter display is produced by a high-speed beam, but it would be harder to deflect if this additional acceleration was applied before the deflection plates.

The speed of the movement of the electron beam across the screen can be very high. Unlike the mechanical pointer of a meter, it is virtually weightless. If the screen is 10 cm across, and the horizontal sweep rate is 0.05 μs per division, the beam is crossing the screen at 720,000 km (447,408 miles) per hour; and many scopes can generate sweeps much faster than that. However, for general troubleshooting purposes we do not need a maximum frequency response greater than 50 MHz (even less for audio). The range from dc to this frequency is termed the *bandwidth*.

Oscilloscope Circuits

Figure 5-4 shows a fine example of a modern service scope, and Figure 5-5 is its block diagram. The main sections are:

1. Attenuators
2. Vertical preamplifier and output amplifier (2 channels)

3. Trigger
4. Sweep logic
5. XY amplifier/horizontal amplifier
6. Front panel controls
7. Power supply and CRT

These sections are described in the following paragraphs, except for number 6, which is covered later under applications.

Attenuators.   These circuits are provided for both channels and include the input coupling, vertical deflection factor, and variable volt/division gain.

The input of the attenuator can be directly coupled to the input terminal (dc coupling), via a capacitor (ac coupling, which blocks dc), or to ground (input terminal disconnected).

With no attenuation, the output signal applied to the vertical deflection plates is such that an input of 5 mV results in a vertical deflection of 1 division. This is the *overall deflection factor.* For settings of the VOLTS/DIV switch above 5 mV/DIV, various combinations of attenuators (voltage dividers) are selected to obtain the other deflection factors indicated on the switch. These attenuators are provided with adjustable resistors and capacitors for recalibration when necessary.

In addition to these fixed attenuators, a variable VOLTS/DIV control is provided that varies the gain of the following amplifier. Normally you should keep this control in its detent (calibrated) position, when the deflection factor will be as indicated on the VOLTS/DIV control. Rotating the variable control counterclockwise lowers the gain of the stage and diminishes the vertical height of the display (it will also be uncalibrated).

Vertical Preamplifier and Output Amplifier.   The single-ended signal from the vertical attenuator is converted into a differential signal for that channel's preamplifier. There are now two signal paths through the rest of this vertical circuit, terminating on the upper and lower deflection plates. Located in the preamplifier is a means of moving the display up or down on the screen by unbalancing the gain of the two paths by operating the vertical position control for that channel. Another gain-adjusting control that affects both paths equally is the X10 magnification control. Both channels provide samples of their signals to the trigger section.

The output signals of the two channels are selected or combined by logic circuits (flip-flops and gates) that are set by the channel switches on the front panel. These allow you to display either channel signal by itself, or both at the same time. When you select BOTH, you also select ADD, ALT, or CHOP. The ADD position causes the two signal voltages to add together. In the ALT position

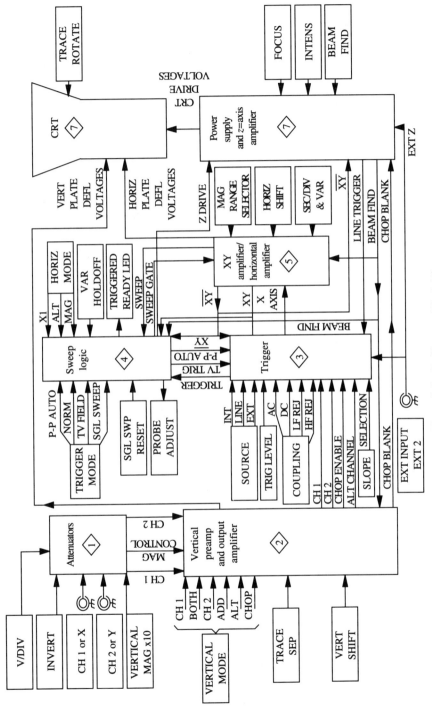

Figure 5-5 Oscilloscope Block Diagram
(Reprinted by permission of Tektronix, Inc.)

63

a signal from the sweep generator causes the channel select flip-flop to toggle, so that the channel 1 and channel 2 signals are displayed on alternate sweeps. In the CHOP position the flip-flop toggles on clock pulses from a multivibrator running at 500 kHz, allowing slow sweeps to be seen simultaneously.

The signals from each preamplifier are then applied to a delay line. This provides a delay of 90 ns, so that the sweep generator has time to produce a sweep before the vertical signal that triggered the sweep reaches the vertical deflection plates.

The vertical output amplifier produces the signal levels on the deflection plates that vertically deflect the electron beam in the CRT. Two other useful controls in this area are the *vertical beam find* and the *alternate sweep separation*. The first one limits the dynamic range of the amplifier, so that it locates the position of an off-screen display by bringing it on-screen. The second provides a means of vertically positioning the alternate magnified sweep with respect to the X1 mode trace during alternate horizontal mode displays.

Trigger.   This circuit develops trigger signals for the sweep generator. They are built up and shaped from internal samples of the signals in channel 1 or channel 2, external signals, or samples of the 60-Hz supply voltage, as selected by the front panel controls. Other controls enable you to select triggering from the leading edge or trailing edge of the signal, to reject high or low frequency signals, and to select the voltage level of the signal where you want triggering to occur. However, the P-P AUTO mode sets the range of the trigger level to conform approximately to the peak-to-peak amplitude of the selected trigger signal when either the *auto* or *TV field* trigger mode is selected. No adjustment of the level control is required in these modes. (The TV field sync circuit provides stable triggering on television vertical sync pulses.)

Sweep Logic.   The sweep logic circuit controls the operation of the sweep generator. When the trigger mode switches are set to either P-P AUTO or TV FIELD and no trigger signal is present, it produces a sweep for reference purposes. In other positions a trigger signal is required. The *single sweep* trigger mode allows only one sweep to be generated after being reset. The SGL SWP RESET button must be pressed for each sweep.

XY Amplifier/Horizontal Section.   This section contains the *sweep generator, X-axis amplifier, horizontal preamplifier,* and *horizontal output amplifier.* The SEC/DIV control selects the *RC* combination of capacitors and resistors that will give the desired sweep time, and the sweep generator produces a linear ramp signal. This is applied to the horizontal preamplifier, where circuits exist that position the display and increase its magnitude by X5, X10, or X50, as required. In the XY mode, the channel 1 signal passes through the XY amplifier to the preamplifier. In this mode, channel 1 provides the trigger signal, and the sweep generator is disabled. The horizontal output amplifier drives the horizontal deflection plates in the CRT. This amplifier also contains a *beam find* circuit similar to that in the vertical amplifier.

Power Supply and CRT.   (The CRT was described earlier.) The power supply has four sections that produce all the voltages required by the other sections of the instrument.

The mains input board and power transformer section comprises the power cord, fuse, on-off switch, power transformer (with switch to select 115 or 230 V_{rms} primary windings), full-wave bridge rectifier, and filter capacitor. It delivers approximately 60 V_{dc} to the preregulator section.

The preregulator section contains a power transistor that is turned on and off by a square wave. The wave's duty cycle varies in accordance with the output voltage to maintain a nominal output of 39.5 V_{dc}.

The series-regulator section has a series-pass transistor that varies its conductance in accordance with the output voltage of the previous section, to reject any remaining ripple. It also supplies 38 V_{dc} to the inverter section.

The inverter section turns its dc input into an output of 39 kHz that is applied to the primary winding of an output transformer. One of its secondary windings supplies the filter and rectifier circuits that produce the CRT high voltages.

Applications

Measuring AC Voltage and Frequency.   Either channel 1 or channel 2 can be used, since only one is required, and they are both alike. Assuming you are using channel 1, its vertical input coupling is set to ac to block any dc that might be present, and the triggering source control is set to CH1 (internal). The channel 1 probe is connected to the input BNC connector for the channel, and its tip to the point in the circuit where the waveform is to be measured (the probe's ground clip is connected to a ground point in the circuit). *Warning:* The maximum voltage that may be measured must not exceed that specified for the scope—usually 400 V_{pk} up to 10 kHz, less at higher frequencies.

Check that the variable controls on the VOLTS/DIV and SEC/DIV controls are in their calibrated detent positions, so that the values read on the graticule will be correct.

Then set the triggering coupling to ac, the slope to positive, and the level control to auto. Adjust the VOLTS/DIV and SEC/DIV controls for a display of convenient size on the screen, and move the waveform into position relative to the graticule, using the position controls, as shown in Figure 5-6.

In this example the VOLTS/DIV control is set at 2 V per division. The waveform has an amplitude of four divisions, so its voltage is $4 \times 2 = 8$ volts peak-to-peak, or 4 volts peak. Its rms voltage is given by

$$V_{rms} = 0.707 \times V_{pk} = 0.707 \times 4 = 2.828 \ V_{rms}.$$

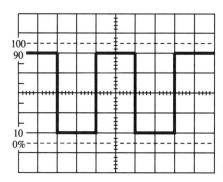

Figure 5-6 Measuring AC Voltage and Frequency

If a 10:1 probe is used, this value will have to be multiplied by 10 to get the real value. However, with this probe, the input impedance increases from 1 megohm shunted by 25 pF to 10 megohms shunted by 15 pF, which makes for a more accurate measurement. (The capacitance values are average for the equipment.)

Set the SEC/DIV to 5 ms, meaning that each division is worth 5 ms. The number of divisions between the same point on two successive cycles of the waveform is four, therefore the time interval between them is 4 × 5 = 20 ms. The frequency is given by

$$f = \frac{1}{20 \times 10^{-3}} = 50 \text{ Hz.}$$

DC Voltage Measurement. For measurement of dc voltages, set the input coupling of the vertical amplifier to ground, so that there is no input, and select automatic triggering. This results in a straight line across the screen, which represents the zero volts level. Using the vertical position control, move this line up or down to coincide with one of the horizontal lines near the bottom of the graticule. Then set the input mode to dc, and apply the probe to the point where the dc voltage is to be measured with the probe's ground clip connected to ground. The line on the screen jumps up in accordance with the voltage present, if the voltage is positive (a negative voltage makes it go down).

It may be necessary to reset the VOLTS/DIV switch to keep the trace on the screen, or to have it rise as far as possible without going off the screen. If the setting of this control is changed, you should reset the zero level, as just explained, in case it has shifted. A slight difference is not unusual for different switch positions.

The voltage is given by the number of divisions between the zero position and the new position of the trace line, multiplied by the probe factor. For instance, in Figure 5-7, the trace line moved up 4.4 divisions. Since the VOLTS/DIV switch was set to 0.1 volt per division, this would represent

+0.44 V_{dc}, or 4.4 V_{dc} if the 10:1 probe was used. If the trace line had shifted downward, the value would be -4.4 V_{dc}, of course.

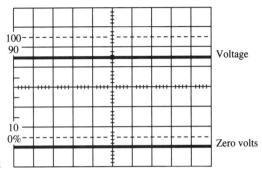

Figure 5-7   DC Voltage Measurement

Accuracy.   If the accuracy of the vertical amplifier is ± 3 percent (a usual figure for scopes), the reliability of these readings is comparable to that of an AMT. Bear in mind that the full-scale accuracy of the AMT is only realized in the upper part of the dial, whereas that of the scope is true anywhere on the screen, except perhaps at the extreme edges. The scope does not, however, have the same accuracy as the DMM, so the DMM should be used if you want an exact measurement.

Amplitude Modulation Measurement.   An amplitude-modulated signal can be displayed if it is within the scope's bandwidth. The screen will look like Figure 5-8. To obtain the percentage of modulation, measure the dimensions A and B on the graticule, and use the following equation.

$$\text{Modulation percentage} = \frac{A - B}{A + B} \times 100$$

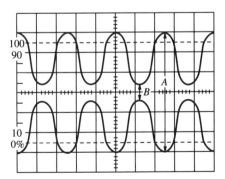

Figure 5-8   Amplitude Modulation Measurement

Using Both Vertical Amplifiers.   You can evaluate the performance of an amplifier by applying a signal to its input, and viewing the input signal with channel 1 and the output signal with channel 2. The amplifier's gain can be measured by comparing the amplitude of the two signals and any distortion introduced in the amplifier by subtracting one signal from the other. Subtracting one signal from the other is done by first adjusting the sizes of the two waveforms so that they are equal, by superimposing one on the other with the scope in the dual mode; then switching to the add mode, and inverting the channel 2 waveform so that it is subtracted from the channel 1 waveform. (To make the waveforms coincide completely, the VOLTS/DIV variable controls can be used, but you must remember this invalidates the calibration of the graticule.) Whatever is left after the channel 2 waveform has been subtracted from the channel 1 waveform line has been introduced by the amplifier. If there is only a straight trace line, then there is no distortion.

X-Y Mode.   On the SEC/DIV switch on this type of scope is a position designated X-Y. When the switch is set to this position, the sweep generator is disconnected, and the channel 2 amplifier is connected in its place. Consequently, whatever the channel 1 amplifier amplifies is applied to the vertical deflection plates, and whatever the channel 2 amplifier amplifies is applied to the horizontal deflection plates. If you apply the same sine wave to both inputs, the display is a sloping line, as shown in Figure 5-9. But if there is a phase difference between the sine wave applied to the channel 1 input and that applied to the channel 2 input, the display will be like that in Figure 5-10. Measuring *A* and *B* and substituting in the following equation gives the sine of the phase angle ϕ.

$$\text{Sine } \phi = \frac{A}{B}$$

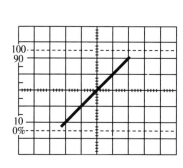

Figure 5-9   X-Y Mode: Two Sine Waves in Phase

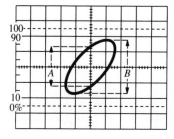

Figure 5-10   X-Y Mode:
Two Sine Waves Not in Phase

If you apply sine waves with different frequencies to the vertical inputs when in the X-Y mode, patterns appear on the screen like those in Figure 5-11. These are called *Lissajous figures*. They indicate the ratio between the frequencies of the two signals. The ratio is given by the number of peaks along the upper horizontal side to the number of peaks along the vertical side.

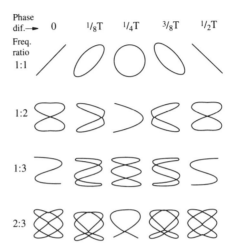

Figure 5-11   Lissajous Figures

The X-Y mode can also be used to test semiconductor junctions in diodes and transistors. Connect the circuit shown in Figure 5-12 to the inputs of channel 1 and channel 2 and across the semiconductor junction. Apply 120 V_{rms} to the transformer primary, bearing in mind the safety precautions given in Chapter 1. If the junction is good, a display similar to that in Figure 5-13 (a) should appear on the oscilloscope screen (adjust VOLTS/DIV and position control as necessary). It may be inverted, but that doesn't matter; you don't need to reverse the connections. However, if the display is like Figure 5-13 (b), (c), or (d), the junction is bad.

Single Sweep.   This mode is used when only one event is expected. The scope is put on standby, and is triggered by the event when it takes place. It can be used to capture an intermittent or transient event and record it on camera.

Photograph.   Polaroid cameras are used for scope photography. The camera is attached to the screen, the method of attachment varying with the model, and the display is photographed. This can be done for single events, as mentioned above or for continuous displays.

Delayed Triggering.   Some scopes have a delayed triggering function by which you can expand a portion of the display. When you select this, part

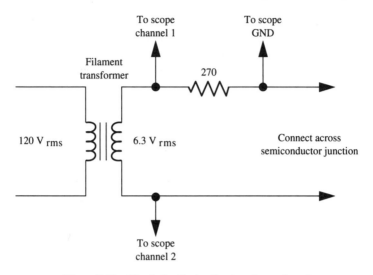

Figure 5–12 Circuit for Testing Semiconductor Junctions

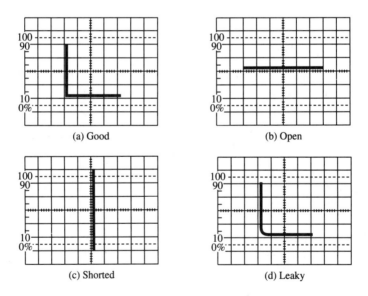

Figure 5–13 Displays Resulting from Using Circuit in Figure 5–12

of the waveform is dimmed, but the rest remains bright. Use a variable control to move the dim portion, until it is positioned just before the point where the expansion is desired. When you have done this, depress a push button to expand the waveform. This function is useful for making more accurate measurements of time intervals.

Calibrator.   The scope contains a multivibrator for generating a square wave with a known amplitude and repetition rate, which is used for checking the accuracy of the vertical attenuators and sweep timing. A connector on the front panel supplies a signal with an amplitude of, say, 0.5 V_{p-p} at 1 kHz. If this is connected to the vertical input and the VOLTS/DIV switch is set to 0.1, the square wave will occupy five vertical divisions, assuming the attenuator is functioning properly and the VOLTS/DIV variable control is set to its calibrated position.

Similarly, if the SEC/DIV control is set to 0.2 ms, each complete cycle of the square wave will occupy five divisions of the graticule, assuming the SEC/DIV variable control is in its calibrated position.

Probe Compensation.   Each probe has a screwdriver adjustment to ensure measurement accuracy. You should check this before making any measurement where accuracy is important. Set the scope up for displaying an ac waveform, and connect each probe in turn to the calibrator output. If the displayed waveform is not flat, as shown in the upper part of Figure 5–14, turn the screwdriver adjustment until it is. Use a low-reactance alignment tool; a metal screwdriver may introduce distortion (check to see that the waveform is still satisfactory after you remove the tool).

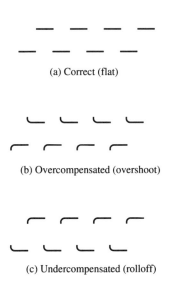

(a) Correct (flat)

(b) Overcompensated (overshoot)

(c) Undercompensated (rolloff)

Figure 5-14   Probe Compensation

6

SIGNAL SOURCES FOR TROUBLESHOOTING

You can best judge the performance of an amplifier (and many other pieces of electronic equipment) by what it does to a test signal. This usually consists of feeding a suitable signal to its input and viewing the output signal with an oscilloscope. The signal can also be traced through the various circuits, as described in Chapter 1. Test signals include *continuous waves, pulses,* and *noise.*

Continuous waves are those that continue their periodic excursions without interruption. Typical continuous waves are shown in Figure 6-1. Their excursions are both positive and negative. They have *amplitude* and *frequency.*

Pulses consist of excursions that are either all positive or all negative. They have a baseline, and the intervals between them are called *baseline dwell times.* They have *amplitude* and *repetition rate.* Typical pulses are shown in Figure 6-2.

Noise signals consist of random impulses distributed over a frequency band. Noise spectra produced by random noise generators are white, pink, and ANSI noise.

Continuous waves are produced by *oscillators, signal generators,* and *function generators.* Pulses are produced by *pulse generators* and *function generators.* Noise is produced by *noise generators.*

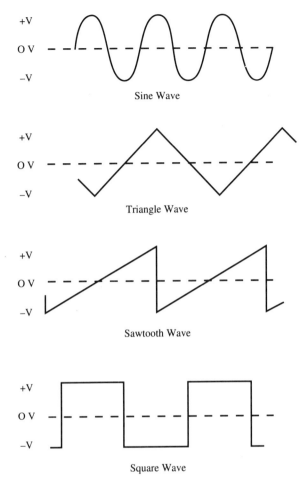

+V
0 V
–V

Sine Wave

+V
0 V
–V

Triangle Wave

+V
0 V
–V

Sawtooth Wave

+V
0 V
–V

Square Wave

Figure 6-1 Typical Continuous Waves

CONTINUOUS WAVES

Characteristics of Continuous Waves

Sine Waves.   The alternating voltage supplied by the electric utility company is in the form of a sine wave. This is because it is generated by rotating machines that operate in principle like the diagram in Figure 6-3. In this example the magnetic field between the north and south poles of the magnet is represented by lines of force. As the wire of the one-turn revolving coil moves through them, an electric current is induced in it with strength proportional to the number of lines of force it cuts per unit of time. Obviously, it cuts most when traveling vertically, least when traveling horizontally. At any instant the strength of the current is in proportion to the position of the coil.

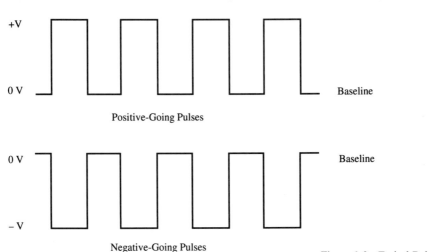

Positive-Going Pulses

Negative-Going Pulses

Figure 6–2   Typical Pulses

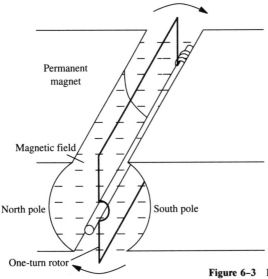

Figure 6–3   Principle of Electric Generator

The coil's position at each instant is defined by its radius H and its perpendicular distance O from the baseline X as shown in Figure 6–4. The ratio $\frac{O}{H}$ is the sine of angle A (hence the term sine wave). When a graph of the rising and falling values of the current is plotted against time it appears as in Figure 6–5. The time could be given in seconds. However, this would vary with the frequency, whereas the angular position of the coil at each instant is the same regardless of frequency. Therefore, the time dimension is given in degrees of arc from 0 to 360 for each complete cycle.

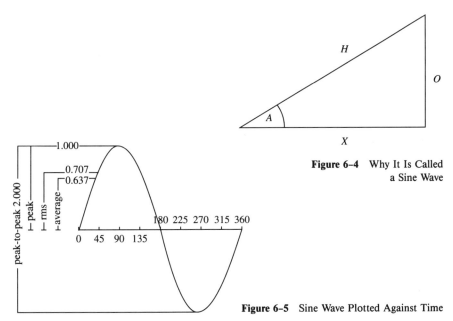

Figure 6-4 Why It Is Called
a Sine Wave

Figure 6-5 Sine Wave Plotted Against Time

Sine waves are found everywhere in nature. The rising and falling pressure waves of a pure sound; the electrical and magnetic waves of a color; the ripples on a pond; are all examples of sine waves. They are not confined to the output of the power company.

In comparing ac to dc, we would like to be able to say that 1 V_{dc} and 1 V_{ac} were equal. But this cannot be stated that simply. The amount of energy in an alternating current that is equal to that in a direct current is less than its peak-to-peak value, because it does not stay at that value all the time. To determine the exact equivalence of dc and ac, early experimenters heated two identical wires, one with a current of 1 ampere dc, and the other with an alternating current that raised it to exactly the same temperature. This was called its *effective* value. It was then said that 1 $A_{effective}$ was equal to 1 A_{dc}, and 1 V_{dc} was equal to 1 $V_{effective}$.

The effective value is mathematically the same as the *root-mean-square* (rms) value of a complete cycle, so the term rms is also used as well as effective. When we say 1 V_{ac} we mean 1 V_{rms}, unless stated otherwise.

The peak value of a sine wave is its rms value multiplied by 1.414, a figure that is also the square root of 2. The peak-to-peak value is twice that, or the rms value multiplied by 2.828.

Square Waves. The rms value of a square wave (Figure 6-6) is the same as its peak value (since it is level throughout each half-cycle), and therefore, half its peak-to-peak value.

Square waves can be shown to consist of all the odd-numbered harmonics out to infinity of a sine wave of the same frequency. In Figure 6-7 you can see how even the fundamental and first two odd harmonics are shaping up that way.

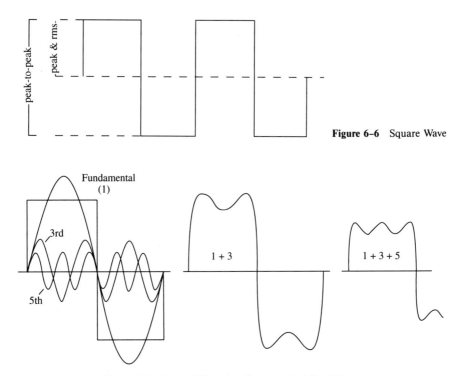

Figure 6–6 Square Wave

Figure 6–7 Square Waves Are Composed of Sine Waves

Triangle Waves and Sawtooth Waves.   If the excursions of a square wave are divided diagonally, it is clear that the resulting triangles have half the area of the rectangles, so their rms values must be half their peak values, or one-fourth of their peak-to-peak values.

Signal Sources for Continuous Waves

Function Generators.   The function generator is widely used because of its capability to produce square waves, sine waves, triangle waves, and pulses. The block diagram in Figure 6–8 shows how it does this.

A square wave is produced by a *multivibrator.* The frequency of this square wave is derived from a capacitor charging through a resistor. The *RC* constant of the two determines the time period of the cycle. The instrument will select resistors and capacitors for the frequency you want by means of the panel controls.

The square wave is applied to an *integrator* to obtain a triangle wave. In this circuit an operational amplifier with a capacitor feedback is used. When a positive square wave excursion is applied to the op-amp input, its output is a rising voltage; when the square wave goes in the opposite direction, the voltage is a falling one.

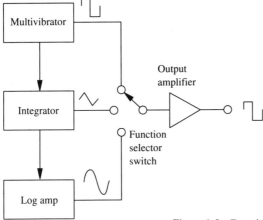

Figure 6-8 Function Generator Block Diagram

The triangle wave is converted to a sine wave by another op-amp circuit that uses the *logarithmic* characteristic of a semiconductor junction in its feedback circuit. This can be supplied by either a diode or a transistor. Any voltage applied to the input of the op-amp results in an output that is in logarithmic proportion to the input. The triangle wave input thus becomes a sine wave output.

Most function generators can also produce pulses, with variable pulse widths and intervals. Some also produce sawtooth waves. These are obtained by modifying the basic square, triangle, and sine waves.

A typical function generator has a frequency range from 0.2 Hz to 2 MHz, with signal amplitude up to 20 V_{p-p}, and a control for varying the pulse duty cycle.

Audio Oscillator.   An audio oscillator generates signals (sine waves and square waves) in the range from 5 Hz to 500 kHz. Although many use a multivibrator, some employ a Wien-bridge or bridged-T oscillator circuit. Audio oscillators were frequently used before function generators became popular, but are used less today.

For many purposes you can use a 60-Hz sine wave as a test signal. This is readily obtained from any ac outlet, using a transformer such as the one shown in Figure 5–12.

Signal Generators.   Whereas the audio oscillator is designed for use at audio frequencies, the signal generator provides radio frequencies that can be amplitude or frequency modulated. The signal is generated by a frequency synthesizer, in which combinations of crystals are used for very exact frequency control.

Basically, the signal generator consists of the oscillator and a power amplifier, separated by a buffer amplifier to isolate the oscillator from variations in the load. Provision is made for modulation, and there is an accurate step attenuator in the output. There is also an output meter to show the output level in volts and decibels.

Signal generators are important in servicing transmitters and receivers used in the Citizen's Band. The Federal Communications Commission (FCC) has strict requirements regarding frequency control, so that precise generators and counters must be used, and the technician must have an FCC license.

PULSES

Pulse Characteristics

Pulses belong in the *time domain,* as opposed to continuous waves, which occupy the *frequency domain.* In both domains, the amplitude of the signal is an important parameter. But in the time domain time intervals come before frequency.

Although a pulse is conventionally depicted as a rectangular excursion from a baseline, in reality it is not possible for it to be that shape. There is no way it can go from the baseline to its upper level, or fall from its upper level back to the baseline in no time at all. Consequently, a pulse is actually trapezoidal, with a more or less flat top parallel to the baseline. This is always the way it appears on a scope, if the scope sweep is fast enough.

Figure 6-9 shows the most important dimensions of a pulse. They are the peak amplitude, the pulse amplitude, the pulse width, the rise time between the 10-percent and 90-percent points, and the fall time between the 90-percent and 10-percent points. One other important parameter not shown in the figure is the pulse period, which is the time between identical points on successive pulses.

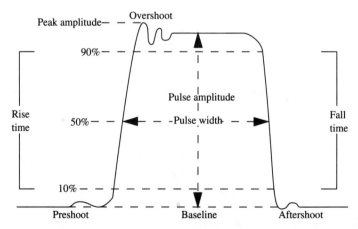

Figure 6-9   Pulse Dimensions

The ratio of the pulse width to the pulse period is called its duty cycle, as shown in Figure 6-10. A succession of pulses is called a pulse train.

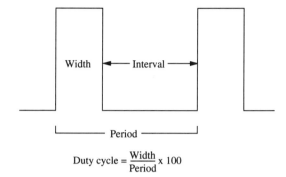

$$\text{Duty cycle} = \frac{\text{Width}}{\text{Period}} \times 100$$

Figure 6-10   Duty Cycle

Sources for Pulses

Some function generators, as already mentioned, can generate pulses. However, a pulse generator, *per se,* is usually more versatile. A good pulse generator not only provides pulses over a wide range of PRR and duty cycles, but it can also shape the pulses in various ways to simulate the characteristics of different logic families. The ability to create pulses with variable rise and fall times is very useful in analyzing the behavior of edge-triggered devices.

A typical pulse generator contains the circuits shown in the block diagram in Figure 6-11. The pulses originate in the repetition rate oscillator, unless an external trigger is used. This oscillator is an astable oscillator, such as a free-running multivibrator. The rate is determined by the setting of the repetition rate control.

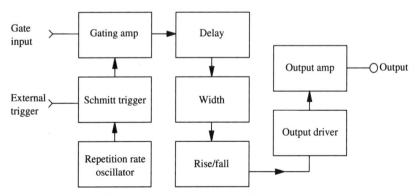

Figure 6-11   Pulse Generator Block Diagram

The signal put out by the repetition rate oscillator is used to activate the Schmitt trigger, or an external source may be used. The Schmitt trigger is a single shot multivibrator that produces an output of fixed amplitude and duration for each input trigger pulse, regardless of its shape, as long as it has the proper polarity and a minimum voltage.

Pulses may be produced continuously or in bursts. The gating circuit, which is a flip-flop, is driven by the signal from the Schmitt trigger when the gate mode switch is in the nongated position. When this switch is rotated to the synchronized position, input synchronizing pulses are applied to the repetition rate oscillator, so that its rate is controlled externally. When in the asynchronized position, external input pulses are applied to the gating circuit and turn it on for the duration of each. In this way, bursts of pulses are "gated" through the gating amplifier.

A second pulse may be generated in the delay circuit. This circuit consists of two flip-flops. If the second flip-flop is switched on, the pulse from the first flip-flop causes it to generate a second pulse, with an interval between it and the first that is variable by means of the delay control. You therefore have the choice of single or double pulses. Double pulses are used for testing memories and counters.

The width circuit adjusts the pulse width, and the rise and fall time circuit gives it its shape. The output amplifier has two channels to give a choice of outputs, positive and negative.

NOISE

Nature of Electrical Noise

Natural electrical noise originates in many ways. For instance, when current flows through a carbon resistor, the haphazard movements of electrons resemble those of pebbles in a mountain torrent. These innumerable random impulses, when amplified, give us the phenomenon we know as noise. When made audible in a speaker or headphones, it sounds like something frying. On an oscilloscope screen it looks like the side elevation of an unkempt lawn.

Unlike a manmade signal, in which each cycle has the same amplitude, frequency, and phase, noise impulses are individually unpredictable. Their characteristics have to be determined by taking the average of large numbers of them. Consequently, we think of noise as having a bandwidth or spectrum, with its energy distributed over this spectrum. This is called its *power density spectrum*.

There is an analogy here to the visible spectrum of light, so that noise that has the same average power density all across its spectrum is called *white noise*. It has constant energy per hertz bandwidth. However, if we pass white noise through a filter that progressively attenuates it toward the high end of the band, it will be like white light passing through a light filter that is progressively more opaque toward the violet end of the spectrum. Such a filter would be a pink filter, and white light would be pink after passing through it. White noise, after passing through a pink noise filter becomes *pink noise*.

Pink noise has constant energy per octave bandwidth. In other words, its energy level decreases by half (down 3 dB) each time the frequency doubles.

You can also have a filter that attenuates on each side of a standard frequency (a bandpass filter) to give an energy level peak at that frequency. The resulting output is known as *ANSI noise*. (ANSI stands for American National Standards Institute.) White, pink, and ANSI noise are shown in graph form in Figure 6–12.

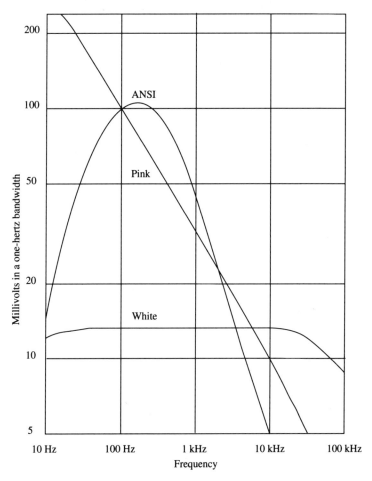

Figure 6–12   White, Pink, and ANSI Noise

The amplitude of each individual impulse is also random. However, naturally occurring phenomena generally are distributed so that they follow a normal (Gaussian) curve. This curve is bell shaped and centered on the average value. It is called the *probability density function* (PDF) of the noise signal. It has absolutely nothing to do with the power density spectrum.

Noise Signal Generators

Noise generators are used to study the effectiveness of receivers in detecting and recovering signals in noise, among other uses. They are not usually required for troubleshooting. However, if you need a source of white noise for this purpose, you will find that a fluorescent tube will do a good job for most practical purposes. Position it so that the receiver can pick up the noise from the tube. You will hear it plainly when not tuned to a station. Then tune to a station and see what happens to the noise.

7

TROUBLESHOOTING WITH
SCOPE AND SIGNAL SOURCE

SIGNAL TRACING

Dynamic Troubleshooting

Signal tracing is a dynamic troubleshooting procedure. Dynamic trouble-shooting is performed under actual operating conditions, as opposed to static testing, when no power is applied.

Signal Tracing, Active and Passive

In Chapter 1 we divided signal tracing into active signal tracing and passive signal tracing. In active signal tracing a signal is provided from an external source, such as a function generator. In passive signal tracing the signal is one that originates within the equipment.

In either case, your oscilloscope is the most versatile of the test instruments you can use. Signal tracing involves tracking a signal stage by stage as it passes through the equipment. Figure 7-1 shows a block diagram that can be applied to virtually any type of electronic equipment. As you can see, a signal source applies a suitable signal to the input device.

The indicating device—your scope—then checks the relative amplitude and quality of the signal at the input and output of each stage. These are the points marked *A, B, C, D, E,* and *F* in Figure 7-1. Each stage, when operating normally, is designed to do something to the signal. If you find that it is doing so correctly, then that stage is working properly. If your scope shows it failing to do so, then you have found the defective stage.

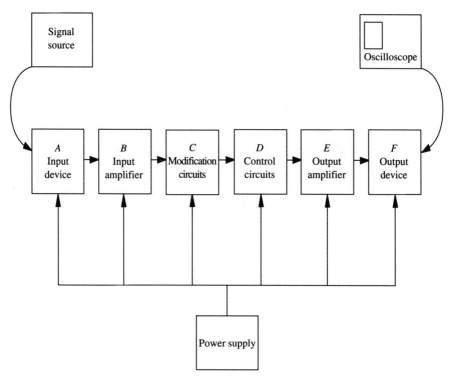

Figure 7-1 Universal Block Diagram

The designations given to the blocks in Figure 7-1 are general ones. In the actual equipment they will vary. Some examples are listed in Table 7-1.

Signal Tracing Technique

Using the signal tracing technique may be summarized as follows.

(1) Turn the equipment on, and allow proper warm-up time.

(2) Apply an adequate test signal to the equipment's input. In a receiver you would obtain a signal from an RF signal generator. In an audio amplifier, this signal may be obtained from a function generator, an audio oscillator, or a tape or a record. In other cases, depending upon the equipment, a pulse generator, or some other signal source, may be suitable. If the equipment generates its own signal, a separate source may not be needed.

(3) Make sure that the connection of the test signal does not have an adverse effect on the circuit. Use a dc blocking capacitor, impedance-matching network, or whatever is required.

(4) Use the minimum signal strength needed to avoid overloading the circuit.

TABLE 7-1 Typical Stages in Widely Used Types of Equipment

Type of Equipment	Input Device	Amplifier Stages	Modification Circuit	Control Circuits	Output Amplifier	Output Device
Public address	Microphone	Preamp	Tone controls	Gain control	Power amp	Speaker
Radio receiver	Antenna, RF stage	IF amp	Second detector	Volume control	Audio section	Speaker
Radio transmitter	Crystal oscillator	Buffer amp	Modulator	"Push-to-talk" button	Power amp and Tank circuit	Antenna
TV receiver (video)	Antenna, tuner	IF amp	Video detector	Picture controls	Video amp	Picture tube

(5) With your scope, check the relative amplitude and quality of the signal at the input and output of each stage.

(6) The test signal should be modified by each stage. For instance, an amplifier should increase its amplitude.

(7) Where necessary, change the type of probe as you trace the signal through the equipment. For instance, use a demodulator probe for RF and IF stages.

(8) If the signal changes in an unexpected fashion, trouble is indicated. You have isolated the defective stage.

Signal Injection

Signal injection is complementary to signal tracing. It can save time if you have reason to suspect a particular stage, because you can go straight to it, instead of going through every other stage first. You may connect your scope to the last stage, or to the output of the suspected stage.

USING WAVEFORMS

In a catastrophic problem, where something has broken down so that the equipment does not perform at all, signal tracing will identify the defective stage by telling you where the signal disappears or is severely weakened. If, for instance, in Figure 7-1 the signal is present at *C,* but absent at *D,* it is obvious something is wrong in the modification circuits. If there is no output at all, you would start looking for an open, short, bad transistor, or similar malfunction.

However, in the type of problem where the complaint is improper performance, identifying the defective stage is not always so simple. Distorted sound from a radio, for example, could not be caused by a dead battery, open resistor, or shorted transistor, because any of these defects would kill the set. The cause of the garbled sound must be something that allows the radio to play, but with impaired performance. Even so, a *major* change in equipment operation, such as weak operation, squealing, motorboating, and so on, in the radio will be fairly easy to track down, but a *minor* change that causes a slight deterioration in overall operation requires a more refined technique. The two most effective ways for analyzing such a situation are by seeing what the stage does to a sine wave or a square wave.

For these tests you need a scope and a function generator. The basic setup is shown in Figure 7-2. The unit under test must be terminated with a load that simulates what it normally works into. For instance, the output of a hi-fi amplifier usually goes to a speaker, and you could use this, of course, if you don't mind the loud noise. But it is easier to concentrate if you substitute a 25- or 50-watt noninductive resistor with a resistance equal to the impedance of the speaker.

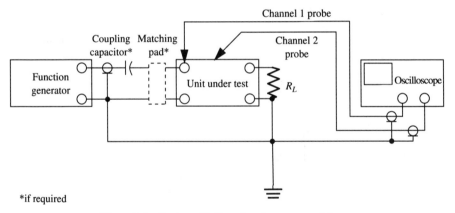

Figure 7-2   Testing with Function Generator and Scope

All the equipment controls are set for normal operation to begin with. The output of the function generator is connected to the unit being tested via a shielded cable, with an isolating capacitor. This capacitor should have a fairly high value, preferably from five to ten times that of any interstage coupling capacitor in the unit being tested. You should also match the output impedance of the generator to the input impedance of the unit being tested. Most generators have output impedances of 50, 75, or 600 ohms, but if the input impedance of the unit is not the same you will need a matching pad, since a mismatch will seriously affect the performance of the unit. Figure 7-3 shows some easily constructed matching pads.

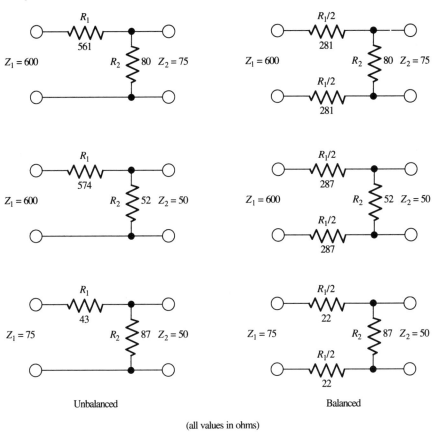

Unbalanced   Balanced

(all values in ohms)

Z_1 must always be the larger impedance.

$$R_1 = [Z_1(Z_1 - Z_2)]^{1/2}$$

$$R_2 = (Z_1 Z_2)/R_1$$

Figure 7-3 Matching Pads

A critical factor that causes improper readings is inadequate grounding. The signal generator, unit being tested, and the scope must all be grounded to each other. Some generators have a balanced output, but the unit being tested has an unbalanced input. The generator will also have a ground terminal, and in this case one of its output terminals should be connected to this so that it, too, has an unbalanced output.

The function generator's output should be adjusted to give an input signal to the unit being tested that is about the same amplitude as the one it would normally receive. The probe for one channel of the scope should be connected here, so that you can see what is going in. The probe for the other channel is applied to the output and intermediate points, so you can see what is happening in the circuits through which the signal passes. The schematic diagram, and your own knowledge of circuit performance, will lead you to expect certain waveforms at the points probed. When you find a deviation from normal, you will then have reason to suspect the circuit between that point and the last point where the signal was normal.

Using a Sine Wave for Testing

Sine waves are used for checking gain and frequency response. If the input and output signals are normal, you can easily verify that the gain at any frequency is as it should be.

Measurement of Gain. You apply a sine wave from a suitable generator to the input of the amplifier or stage. The amplitude of the sine wave should be about what the normal input signal would be.

Connect the probe from the channel 1 vertical amplifier of the scope to the input of the amplifier, and adjust the VOLTS/DIV control for a display of convenient size, as shown in Figure 7-4 (a). Suppose that this gives a display of 6 divisions, with a 10 times probe and the VOLTS/DIV control set to 10 mV. Then the peak-to-peak amplitude of the sine wave must be 0.6 V.

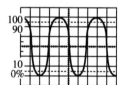

Figure 7-4 (a)   Input Signal Applied to Scope Channel 1

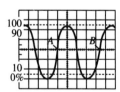

Figure 7-4 (b)   Output Signal Applied to Scope Channel 2

The probe for the channel 2 vertical amplifier of the scope is connected to the output of the amplifier or stage, and the scope mode changed to display channel 2. After the VOLTS/DIV control has been adjusted, a display like the one in Figure 7-4 (b) appears. The amplitude of the sine wave is 5.2 divisions, and the setting of the VOLTS/DIV control is 0.1 V with a 10 times probe, so the amplitude of the signal is now 5.2 V. The voltage gain A_v of the amplifier is given by

$$A_v = \frac{5.2}{0.6} = 8.7.$$

Frequency Check. The frequency is easily checked by counting the divisions and fractions of a division on the horizontal scale between identical points on two successive cycles of the displayed sine wave. In Figure 7–4 (b) there are 4.5 divisions between A and B. Assuming that the SEC/DIV (or TIME/DIV) control is set to 0.1 ms per division, the time interval between A and B must be $4.5 \times 0.1 = 0.45$ ms. The frequency is the reciprocal of this, of course, or 2.222 kHz. The pocket calculator makes short work of this. The most important thing to remember is that the time interval between A and B must be entered in *seconds,* either as 0.00045 or as 0.45×10^{-3}; then you just take the reciprocal. (If you are using a calculator that does not have a reciprocal $(1/x)$ key, press the keys $1 \div 0.00045$ to get the same result. However, you should get a calculator that has $1/x$, as well as other functions, such as pi (π), square, square root, sin, cos, tan, log, and ln$x$ because they are being used continuously in electronics calculations.)

Checking Frequency Response. If you perform the gain test given above for several frequencies, you can verify the amplifier's frequency response over its frequency range. Be sure to maintain the same level of input for each frequency.

Apply one frequency at a time to the input. Connect the scope's channel 1 to the input also, and adjust the function generator's output to give a display on the scope that fits exactly between two graticule lines, as shown in Figure 7–4 (a).

Connect the scope's channel 2 to the output, and observe the display. Write down the amplitude and frequency.

Then readjust the function generator for the next frequency. If necessary, readjust the signal level to keep the channel 1 display exactly between the two graticule lines as before. Then write down the amplitude and frequency shown on the channel 2 display.

Continue this procedure until you have gone through the range of frequencies you wish to cover. Then make a graph of the values you have found. It should look like the one in Figure 7–5.

Using a Square Wave for Testing

A more rapid check of overall frequency response can be made using square waves instead of sine waves. This check does not produce a graph like Figure 7–5, but takes advantage of the fact that a square wave consists of the fundamental frequency and all its odd harmonics, so that the amplifier's entire frequency range is checked qualitatively (but not quantitatively) in one measurement.

The test setup is the same as it is for sine wave testing, except that the function generator is reset for a square wave output. It is important, however, to keep the amplitude of the input signal as low as possible, consistent with getting an adequate response, because it is possible to overload the circuit

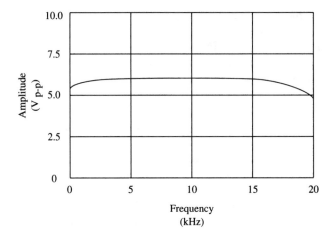

Figure 7-5   Frequency Response Graph

without realizing it. With a sine wave you would notice the flattened peaks, but a square wave is flat-topped anyway, so overloading the circuit would give you even flatter peaks, which might be better looking than they really are.

The appearance of the output square wave should be the same as that of the input. However, it may be distorted in various ways if the circuits through which it passes are not amplifying all frequencies equally, as shown in Figure 7-6.

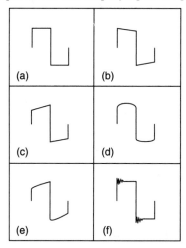

Figure 7-6   Various Types of Square Wave Response

The top (and bottom) of each square wave excursion gives a lot of information. The higher frequencies form the leading edge, so that if this portion is rounded it means that these frequencies are not being amplified as well. If the top slopes upward from the leading edge to the trailing edge (from left to right on your scope), it means that the amplifier's response improves as the frequency decreases. If the slope goes downward, it tells you that the lower frequencies are receiving even less amplification than the higher ones. A guide to the interpretation of square wave distortions is given in Table 7–2.

TABLE 7–2   Square Wave Distortion Reference Guide

Square Wave Input	Output Waveform	Figure Number	Interpretation
50–100 Hz	Like input	7–6 (a)	Circuit operation normal
	Slanting down	7–6 (b)	Poor low frequency response
	Sharp pulse	—	Extremely poor low frequency response
	Slanting up	7–6 (c)	Accentuated low frequency response
	Rounded top	7–6 (d)	Accentuated response at fundamental frequency of square wave
	Rounded leading edge	7–6 (e)	Reduced upper frequency response
	Damped oscillation	7–6 (f)	Peak in middle range of frequencies
500–2500 Hz	Like input	7–6 (a)	Circuit operation normal
	Slanting down	7–6 (b)	Poor low frequency response
	Sharp pulse	—	Extremely poor low and middle frequency response
	Slanting up	7–6 (c)	Accentuated response at middle frequencies
	Rounded top	7–6 (d)	Accentuated response at fundamental frequency of square wave
	Rounded leading edge	7–6 (e)	Reduced upper frequency response
	Damped oscillation	7–6 (f)	Peak at high frequencies
5 kHz–20 kHz	Like input	7–6 (a)	Circuit operation normal
	Slanting down	7–6 (b)	Poor medium frequency response
	Sharp pulse	—	Extremely poor medium frequency response
	Slanting up	7–6 (c)	Accentuated response at upper frequencies
	Rounded top	7–6 (d)	Accentuated response at fundamental frequency of square wave
	Rounded leading edge	7–6 (e)	Poor high frequency response
	Damped oscillation	7–6 (f)	Peak in response at frequency beyond normal (desired) range

When you have isolated the stage where the malfunction occurs, you will be looking for (1) coupling or emitter bypass capacitors that have changed value for Figure 7–6 (b) and (c) distortion; (2) coupling or emitter capacitors that are completely open for sharp pulses; feedback problems might also be responsible for distortions of the types seen in Figure 7-6 (d) and (f); excessive distributed capacitance for Figure 7-6 (e) distortion; and (3) poor shielding, lead dress, and grounding problems for loss of the upper frequencies.

Distortion

Undesired changes in waveforms, such as those just described, are called distortion. Any circuit is designed to modify the input signal in a certain way, and since nothing is perfect, a small degree of distortion is inevitable. However, the specifications for the circuit will permit only a limited amount, so that anything above that is a malfunction. This is especially true of amplifier and loudspeaker systems, where faithful reproduction of music and speech is required. There are four main types of distortion: amplitude, frequency, phase, and cross modulation.

Amplitude Distortion.   The output signal amplitude of a transistor is linearly proportional to the input signal amplitude over a limited range. As soon as the limits of that range are exceeded, the output is no longer a true replica of the input. Amplitude distortion has been introduced. For this reason, the circuit is usually designed with negative feedback to prevent the transistor from being overdriven.

However, it is still possible for the transistor to be overdriven if too strong a signal is applied to its input. If it is driven into saturation, further increase in input signal amplitude produces little effect in the output.

Another form of amplitude distortion arises with Class B transistor power amplifiers. In this type of amplifier the input impedance varies inversely with the emitter current. For low values of current this may become considerable compared with the driver impedance. The result is distortion of the output waveform. This type of amplitude distortion is known as *crossover distortion.*

These remarks, then, indicate where to look for the cause of amplitude distortion. If the input signal is within the specified parameters for the amplifier, distortion should not occur unless there is a malfunction in the feedback circuit.

Frequency Distortion.   This type of distortion is found in all amplifiers, but they are designed to minimize it as far as possible. Reactive circuit components do not allow all frequencies to be amplified to the same degree. In most cases the reactive component is a capacitor, since few inductors are used in modern circuits. The square wave is particularly good at revealing this problem, as we have seen, since it is composed of a fundamental and many harmonic frequencies.

Phase Distortion.   The cause of phase distortion is the same as the cause of frequency distortion. A reactive component gives different phase shifts to different frequencies. Fortunately, the ear is more tolerant of phase shift than of the other forms of distortion, but the fact that we do not encounter this complaint so often does not mean that it is not there.

Cross Modulation.   This is caused when two input signals of different frequencies are applied to a nonlinear transistor stage. The output will contain the fundamentals and harmonics of both signals, which will heterodyne with each other to produce new sum and difference frequencies that were not in the input signal. This distortion, which is also called *intermodulation distortion,* can be worse than amplitude distortion.

Feedback Circuits.   The feedback circuits designed to reduce distortion return a portion of the output signal to the input, and, because it is of opposite phase to the input signal, it subtracts from it. Hence it is called negative or degenerative feedback.

In an amplifier, negative *current* feedback is produced by an unbypassed emitter resistor; negative *voltage* feedback is produced by connecting the base voltage divider to the collector instead of to the supply voltage, as shown in Figure 7-7.

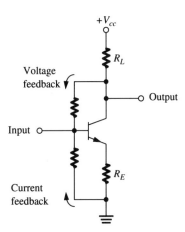

Figure 7-7   Negative Feedback

8

LOGIC CIRCUIT TEST
EQUIPMENT

DIGITAL ELECTRONICS

Digital circuits process information encoded as voltage or current *levels*. The code used is the binary system, in which there are two levels that are handled by a simple on-off switch type of operation. Test equipment for use in such circuits is required only to indicate which of the two levels is present.

Logic Probe

The logic probe, as shown in Figure 8-1, has light emitting diodes that respond to the voltage level present at a point in a circuit. For instance, if the level is high, a red LED lights; if it is low, a green one lights. If, instead of a dc voltage, a pulse train is present, a yellow LED blinks.

As shown in Figure 8-2, the probe tip is connected to a comparator, which compares the input voltage with the supply voltage in the circuit being tested. If this is a circuit using bipolar transistor logic, the supply voltage is generally $+5$ V_{dc}. A high level will be between 2.25 and 5 V_{dc}, a low level below 0.8 V_{dc}. The logic family switch is set to DTL/TTL (diode-transistor logic/transistor-transistor logic). The output of the comparator is high or low, according to its input, and the red or green LED lights as appropriate.

If the logic family switch is set to CMOS (complementary metal-oxide-semiconductor logic) the reference voltages for the comparator change to over 70 percent of the supply voltage (high) and less than 30 percent (low). In CMOS circuits the supply voltage can be as high as 35 V_{dc}.

Figure 8-1   Using a Logic Probe

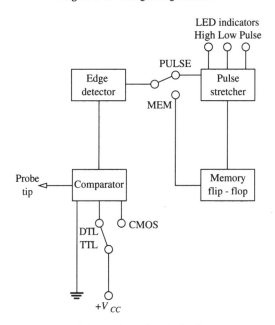

Figure 8-2   Logic Probe Block Diagram

A transition from positive to negative, or vice versa, causes the edge detector to activate the pulse stretcher circuit. This converts the transition to a pulse with a duration of 0.3 second, which makes the yellow LED blink. If the transitions are not less than 5 microseconds apart, both the red and green LEDs light also. The probe shows the yellow LED blinking at a 3 Hz rate, and the red and green LEDs apparently steady. The meaning is a signal with a frequency of not more than 100 kHz, and a duty cycle of 50 percent (in other words, a square wave). If the frequency is higher, there is no indication from the red and green LEDs.

Pulse trains also have transitions and cause the yellow LED to blink in a similar manner, but their duty cycles may be other than 50 percent. If the duty cycle is less than 15 percent, only the green LED will light, but if it is increased above 15 percent, the red LED will begin to glow. Conversely, if the duty cycle is over 85 percent, only the red LED will light, but if it is decreased below 85 percent, the green LED will begin to glow.

If the MEM/PULSE switch is set to MEM, a level transition is applied to the pulse memory flip-flop. The flip-flop latches to hold the transition pulse until further notice, and the yellow LED is turned on. It is turned off by resetting the MEM/PULSE switch to PULSE. This flip-flop is activated by a transition of either polarity, and also by touching the probe tip to the test point. Consequently, the tip should be in contact with the test point *before* setting the switch to the MEM position.

This description of the operation of the logic probe shown in Figure 8–1 is typical of logic probes in general, although there may be variations in their specifications. For instance, one probe may be capable of responding to pulses with a width as low as 50 nanoseconds, while another can detect pulses with a width of only 15 ns.

Homemade Logic Probe

You can make a simple logic probe that will indicate voltage levels and relatively low frequency signals in TTL circuits, using the device shown in Figure 8–3. A 7404 IC will supply the two inverters, and the rest of the circuit consists of a pair of LEDs, one red, the other green, with suitable current-limiting resistors. These can be mounted in a pencil-like arrangement (made of any kind of tube with an internal diameter of half an inch, or so), with a probe tip at one end, and a pair of leads with alligator clips at the other for attaching to circuit V_{cc} and ground. Connect all the unused inputs to V_{cc}.

This probe will see any voltage of 2 V_{dc} or over as a high level (red LED lights), and any voltage 0.8 V_{dc} or below as a low level (green LED lights). A slow pulse train will cause both LEDs to light alternately or glow with reduced brightness.

Pulses may be supplied by a function generator, a pulse generator, a logic pulser, or from within the circuit itself. The logic pulser looks like a logic probe, but generates single pulses or continuous pulse trains for application wherever wanted.

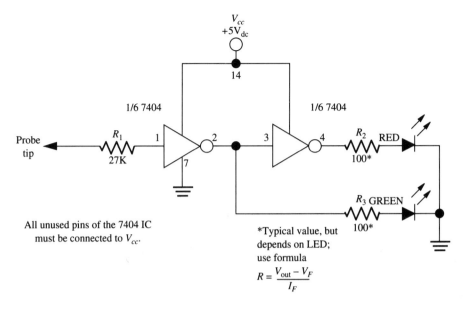

Figure 8-3   Homemade Logic Probe

Logic Pulser

The logic pulser looks very much like the logic probe, and they can be used together very conveniently, one in each hand. A typical pulser has a probe tip that applies a single pulse, or a pulse train, to the desired point in the circuit when the push button is pressed. When the push button is pressed for less than one second, a single pulse is output; if it is held down for longer, a train of pulses at 100 Hz results. An LED lights to indicate the output. There is also a switch for selecting TTL or CMOS, as in the logic probe.

Homemade Pulser

You can make a pulser that puts out one pulse at a time by using the circuit shown in Figure 8-4. As you can see, it consists of a battery, a switch, a couple of resistors, and a capacitor.

With the switch in the *A* position, the capacitor is connected to the positive battery terminal; when it is in the *B* position it is connected to the negative terminal. In this way, you can get a single pulse of either logic level when you apply the pulser tip to the test point.

You can use this pulser with a logic probe, or with an oscilloscope; but remember, it only puts out one pulse at a time.

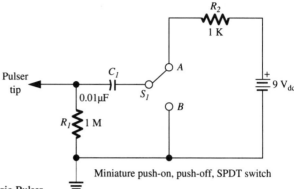

Figure 8-4 Homemade Logic Pulser

Logic Monitor

Another useful device is a logic monitor. This is a spring-loaded clip that clamps over a dual in-line package (DIP) IC like a clothes pin, simultaneously contacting each pin up to a maximum of 16. The logic state of each pin contacted is displayed by a corresponding LED, which lights for a high level or remains unlit for a low level. Since the supply voltage goes to one of the pins of the IC, and another is connected to ground, no separate power lead is required for this monitor.

Another type of monitor has the clip that goes over the IC at the end of a 16-conductor ribbon cable. The cable leads to a small case with a 16-LED display, a TTL/CMOS switch, and a thumb wheel for adjusting the threshold level at which the LEDs will light. This ensures that no LED will light at a lower level than the actual threshold voltage of the device being tested. Unlike the previously described logic monitor, it obtains its power from an ac adapter instead of the circuit.

Test Clips

Contacting an IC pin with a probe tip is fairly easy, but it is often difficult, if not impossible, to connect a test lead to an IC pin, especially when the pin is mounted on a densely populated circuit board. A test clip is a device made to slip over the IC and reliably contact each of its pins, with a corresponding set of easily accessed pins on its upper edges.

LOGIC ANALYSIS

The instruments described so far are the logic equivalents of multimeters, but more elaborate test equipment is required for analysis of data handling. Logic analysis is the counterpart of signal tracing, and it requires data analyzers and data generators. Such test equipment is sophisticated and costly, so it is seldom found in the ordinary service shop. However, there is no other good way to actively troubleshoot complex digital circuitry.

Data Analyzer

Unlike analog circuits, where we can say there is only one "data" channel, digital circuits may handle bytes, or "words," with up to 32 bits (or more), each bit traveling in its own channel. To track each bit through a large number of ICs would be a tedious and time-consuming operation, so in that sort of equipment it is preferable to transmit the entire set of bits simultaneously, displaying the output on the data analyzer. Successive sets are generated in a data generator, which may be part of the data analyzer, a separate instrument, or an internal source in the equipment being tested. The simplest way of doing this would be to generate a succession of words in the form,

$$
\begin{aligned}
&00000000 \\
&00000001 \\
&00000010 \\
&00000011 \\
&\dots\dots \\
&11111111
\end{aligned}
$$

assuming an 8-channel device.

If these are displayed without error on the data analyzer, it is obvious the equipment is working properly. The analyzer may be programmed to stop if an error is encountered. This may be a failure to transmit a bit in one of the channels, or a "glitch" that causes a bit to be falsely transmitted. (A glitch is any stray pulse or spike that shouldn't be there.) The data analyzer displays the data in 1s and 0s, as above, or in pulse trains.

Data Generator

The data generator outputs words at various rates and of various lengths up to 256 bits. The signal parameters are adjustable, enabling you to simulate degraded signals so that the worst conditions can be evaluated.

9

TROUBLESHOOTING LOGIC
CIRCUITS

NATURE OF LOGIC CIRCUITS

Analog and Digital Circuits Compared

The main difference between analog and digital circuits is in their modes of operation. Analog circuits handle analog signals, and the individual transistor stages generally operate in a linear manner. That is to say, the transistors are biased and the amplitudes of the input signals are such that the stages operate in the linear portions of their response curves, without straying into saturation or cutoff.

In digital circuits exactly the opposite takes place. For the most part, the transistors perform like single-pole, single-throw switches, toggling between the two states of saturation (conducting) and cutoff (nonconducting), according to whether the voltage applied to their bases is high or low.

Logic Functions

The simplest switch consists of a single transistor, as in Figure 9–1. Only one of two voltage levels may be applied to its base. When a high level (approximately the same level as the supply voltage V_{cc}) is applied, the transistor saturates, so that the lower end of the load resistor R_L is grounded. Consequently, the output voltage is zero. Conversely, when a low voltage (zero) is applied to the base, the transistor cannot conduct (the base-emitter junction is reverse biased), so no current flows through R_L, and the collector voltage is the same as the supply voltage V_{cc}.

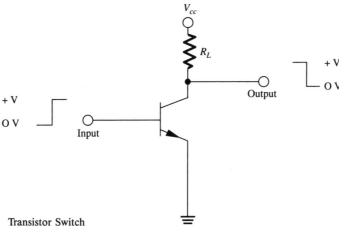

Figure 9-1   Transistor Switch

We really don't care what this circuit consists of as long as it performs as a switch. It could be contained in a box, with just four connections to the outside (input, output, V_{cc}, and ground). It is generally symbolized as a triangle with a small circle, as shown in Figure 9-2. This is the symbol for an amplifier, with the circle added to indicate that it is *not* an analog amplifier. It is called an *inverter,* because it generates the complement of the input. We don't bother to show the V_{cc} and ground connections in this kind of diagram.

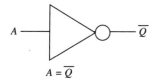

Truth Table

A	Q
1	0
0	1

Figure 9-2   Inverter Symbol and Truth Table

Beside the symbol in Figure 9-2 is a small table, called a *truth table.* Its two columns are labeled A and Q. A is the input, and Q is the output. In either column, a 1 indicates a high voltage level, a 0 indicates a low level or zero voltage. This is the convention for *positive logic,* which is the most widely used. Where there is a 0 in the A column, there is a 1 in the Q column, and vice versa.

Beneath the symbol is a statement $A = \bar{Q}$. The bar over the Q means that Q is equal to the *complement* of A. This is read "A equals not Q," for which reason an inverter is also called a *NOT gate.*

However, the term *gate* is more usually employed for circuits in which two or more transistor switches are arranged to allow high or low outputs according to specified inputs. For instance, if two switches are connected in series, it is obvious that both must be closed if current is to flow. As shown in Figure 9–3, switches *A and B* must be closed for the lamp *Q* to light. This is therefore called an *AND gate,* in which $A \cdot B = Q$. The dot between *A* and *B* means "and." In other words, output *Q* is high when both inputs *A* and *B* are high. The symbol and truth table for an AND gate are given in Figure 9–4.

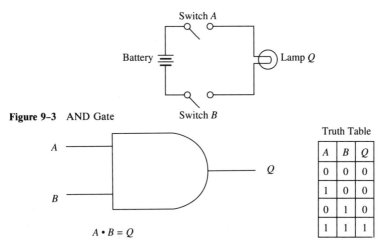

Figure 9–3   AND Gate

Figure 9–4   AND Gate Symbol and Truth Table

Truth Table

A	B	Q
0	0	0
1	0	0
0	1	0
1	1	1

$A \cdot B = Q$

However, if the switches are in parallel, as in Figure 9–5, closing either will suffice to light *Q;* or $A + B = Q$, where the plus sign means "or." This arrangement is therefore called an *OR gate.* Its symbol and truth table are shown in Figure 9–6.

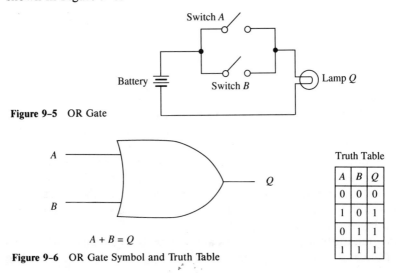

Figure 9–5   OR Gate

Figure 9–6   OR Gate Symbol and Truth Table

Truth Table

A	B	Q
0	0	0
1	0	1
0	1	1
1	1	1

$A + B = Q$

If an inverter is added to an AND gate, the output is complemented, or $A \cdot B = \bar{Q}$. This is called a *NAND gate*. Instead of drawing the complete inverter symbol, the inversion is shown by the addition of a small circle, as shown in Figure 9-7.

Truth Table

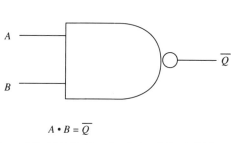

$A \cdot B = \bar{Q}$

Figure 9-7   NAND Gate Symbol and Truth Table

A	B	Q
0	0	1
0	1	1
1	0	1
1	1	0

Similarly, an OR gate can have an inverter built in to give a *NOR gate*. The NOR gate's symbol and truth table are shown in Figure 9-8.

Truth Table

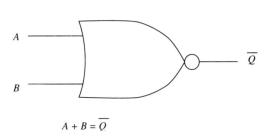

$A + B = \bar{Q}$

Figure 9-8   NOR Gate Symbol and Truth Table

A	B	Q
0	0	1
0	1	0
1	0	0
1	1	0

Each of these gates is shown with two inputs, but they may have more. The truth table will have an additional column for each extra input. Regardless of the circuitry, the symbols are what count. And these basic circuits are the building blocks for more elaborate circuits, which may be incorporated in an IC. An IC is usually drawn as a rectangle (except operational amplifiers, which are shown as a triangle), without any attempt to depict the internal circuits. This is unnecessary, because the truth table tells you what is supposed to happen.

Gates are like push button switches. They respond to an impulse, and maintain that response until the stimulus is removed. Another class of "switch" responds to an impulse, but maintains the response after the impulse is removed, like a toggle switch. It is therefore a memory device. It takes a new impulse to change it. This type of circuit is called a *latch*.

A latch is shown in Figure 9-9. It consists of two NAND gates cross-connected so that the output of each NAND gate is fed back to one of the inputs of the other. The remaining inputs are labeled R and S, for *reset* and *set*. From the truth table you can see that when R is high and S is low, $\bar{Q}$ is low and Q is high. $\bar{Q}$'s low output is fed back to NAND 2's second input, so that both inputs are low, resulting in a high output at Q. This is fed back to NAND 1's second input, so both inputs are high, and the output at $\bar{Q}$ is low. However, confusion arises if both inputs are high, so this situation must be avoided. A similar latch can be constructed using NOR gates.

Indeterminate conditions are avoided by using clocked *flip-flops,* such as the D and *J-K* flip-flops shown in Figure 9-10. A change of state of the outputs is allowed only on a clock pulse.

Flip-flops are often arranged in groups to perform such functions as counting, storage, or shifting data from serial to parallel format. Figure 9-11 shows a shift register, and Figure 9-12 shows a ripple counter.

The binary number system is used in digital circuits, because it fits the high and low voltage convention. Table 9-1 shows equivalent decimal and binary numbers up to decimal 31. The decimal value of each binary 1 depends upon which column it is in. Each column has twice the value (weight) of the one to its right, except the first column on the right, which has a weight of 1, and the 1 or 0 appearing in it is called the *least significant bit* (LSB). The term *bit* is short for "binary digit."

TABLE 9-1   Equivalent Decimal and Binary Numbers

Decimal	Binary	Decimal	Binary
0	0	16	10000
1	1	17	10001
2	10	18	10010
3	11	19	10011
4	100	20	10100
5	101	21	10101
6	110	22	10110
7	111	23	10111
8	1000	24	11000
9	1001	25	11001
10	1010	26	11010
11	1011	27	11011
12	1100	28	11100
13	1101	29	11101
14	1110	30	11110
15	1111	31	11111

Binary numbers are often written in blocks of four, with leading zeros. For example, 20 would be 0001 0100. The number on the left is the *most significant bit* (MSB).

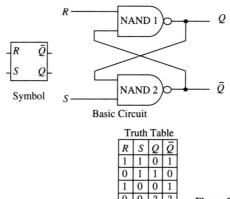

Truth Table

R	S	Q	$\bar{Q}$
1	1	0	1
0	1	1	0
1	0	0	1
0	0	?	?

Figure 9-9   Latch

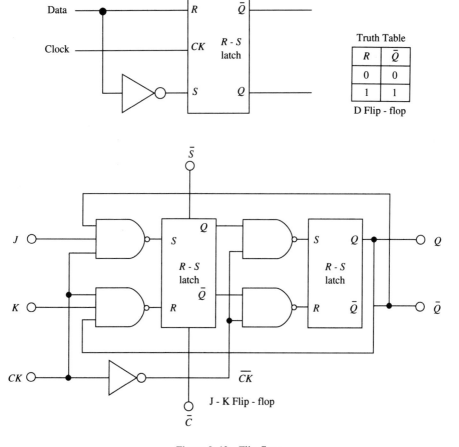

Truth Table

R	$\bar{Q}$
0	0
1	1

D Flip - flop

Figure 9-10   Flip-flops

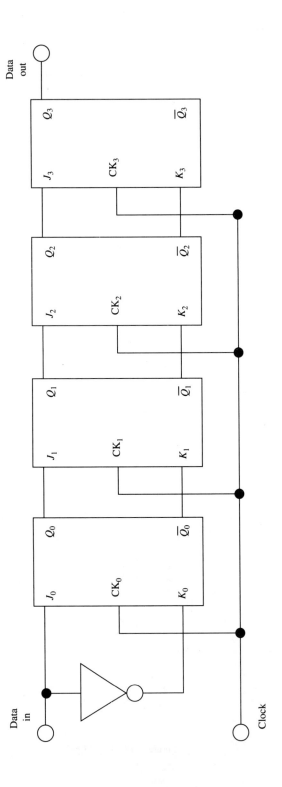

Figure 9–11 Shift Register

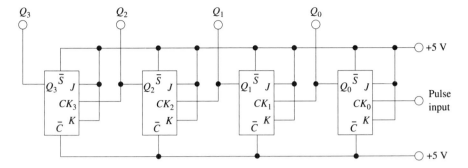

Truth Table

Pulse Input	Status of Q Outputs (1 = high, 0 = low)*			
	Q_3	Q_2	Q_1	Q_0
0	0	0	0	0
1	0	0	0	1
2	0	0	1	0
3	0	0	1	1
4	0	1	0	0
5	0	1	0	1
6	0	1	1	0
7	0	1	1	1
8	1	0	0	0
9	1	0	0	1
10	1	0	1	0
11	1	0	1	1
12	1	1	0	0
13	1	1	0	1
14	1	1	1	0
15	1	1	1	1

On the 16th pulse all Q outputs return to 0000, and the count is repeated. More flip-flops are required to count to higher numbers. The J, K, $\bar{S}$, and $\bar{C}$ inputs are held high at all times, except when the $\bar{C}$ is set low momentarily to clear the flip-flops.

*Binary count

Figure 9–12   Ripple Counter

Logic Families

Of the various methods of manufacturing digital ICs, four predominate. Table 9–2 shows their main characteristics.

TABLE 9–2 Characteristics of Principal Logic Families

	TTL	ECL	MOS	CMOS
Supply voltage	+ 5.00 V	− 8 to − 10 V	− 10 to − 30 V	+ 5.0 to + 10.0 V
"0" level	0.70 V	− 1.85 V[a]	− 0.3 V[a]	0.5 to 1.0 V[a]
"1" level	2.15 V	− 0.70 V[a]	− 10.3 V[a]	2.5 to 5.8 V[a]
Maximum frequency[b]	15 MHz	50 to 150 MHz	2 to 10 MHz	1 to 1.5 MHz

[a] Typical value.

[b] Maximum frequency indicates the speed that each takes to turn on and off.

Table 9–2 tells you that these families are not compatible with each other, although some types of TTL and CMOS are. When different logic families must work together, interface circuits are required to make this possible.

The most widely used logic families are the TTL and the CMOS, which have been standardized by all manufacturers. The TTL family is characterized by a system of four numbers beginning with 74- (54- for military versions); CMOS numbers also have four figures beginning with 40- or 74C- (military 54C-). Some popular types are listed in Table 9–3.

TABLE 9–3 Popular TTL and CMOS ICs

TTL		CMOS	
Number	Description	Number	Description
7400	4 2-input NAND gates	4001	4 2-input NOR gates
7404	6 inverters	4011	4 2-input NAND gates
7408	4 2-input AND gates	4013	Dual flip-flop
7447	BCD decoder/driver	4017	Decade counter
7490	BCD counter	4049	6 inverters (buffers)

These numbers will usually be prefixed by the letters identifying its manufacturer. A list of these is shown in Table 9–4.

The four figure group will often be broken by the insertion of one or more letters between the first two and the last two figures. An *H* indicates high speed, an *L* indicates low power, an *S* indicates the IC is made by the Schottky process. The letters *LS* indicate a low power Schottky device. Suffixes also are used to indicate package type. The most common package is the plastic dual in-line (DIP), denoted by the suffix *N*.

TABLE 9–4   IC Manufacturer Identification Prefix Codes

Prefix	Manufacturer	Prefix	Manufacturer	Prefix	Manufacturer
BA	Rohm	MOC	Motorola	SLP	Sanyo
CEX	Control Electronics	MPS	Motorola	SN	Texas Instruments
DAC	National Semiconductor	MRF	Motorola	TA	Toshiba
FND	Fairchild	MU	Motorola	TIL	Texas Instruments
FRL	Litronix	MV	General Instrument	TIP	Motorola
ICM	Intersil	NE	Signetics	TLO	Texas Instruments
LF	National Semiconductor	NSM	National Semiconductor	TL	Texas Instruments
LM	National Semiconductor	PCIM	PC International	TLG	Toshiba
MA	Motorola	S	American Micro Systems	TLR	Toshiba
MC	Motorola	SAD	Reticon	VN	Siliconix
MJ	Motorola	SE	Signetics	XC	Xciton
MM	National Semiconductor,	SEL	Sanken		
	Motorola, or Teledyne	SCS	Spectronics		

TROUBLESHOOTING LOGIC CIRCUITS

How Digital ICs Fail

ICs are vulnerable to excessive voltage, temperature, and mechanical mistreatment, more so than transistors. And when they fail, they fail completely. There is no gradual deterioration. However, you don't really need to care about the exact nature of the internal failure, since there is no way to examine the inside of an IC, but you should be concerned about what caused it, since merely replacing the IC may only result in another failure within a short time.

Excessive voltage can be in the power supply. There may be a defect in it, such as a failure of the voltage regulator, or an open filter capacitor that allows ac hum to ride on the dc supply voltage. If you suspect the power supply may be at fault, your oscilloscope will show you if there is hum present. The ac function of your DMM or AMT will also reveal the presence of ac, though not as well as the scope.

Excessive input signal voltage is often caused by static electricity. CMOS ICs are particularly at risk here. You have to be very careful in working with a printed circuit board that has CMOS ICs on it, because stray high voltages can be introduced by you, yourself (voltage you pick up in dry weather from various sources), or by using a leaky ungrounded 60-hertz soldering iron. Static can also be caused by nearby lightning strikes. These occurrences often cause the demise of several ICs at the same time.

Temperature problems are usually due to overheating. This can arise from poor ventilation, when the ventilating louvers have been blocked by poor placement, or from heavy accumulation of dust. In some cases, failure of a cooling fan may have this effect. Another cause is when a heat sink is not making proper contact with the component it is serving, or, in some cases, with a metal chassis. You can get an idea of whether overheating is taking place by touching ICs with your fingertip—gingerly! If an IC is running very hot, something is wrong, since most ICs are specified for a maximum operating temperature of 70° C (158° F). This is the temperature of very hot water, and few ICs can last long at it.

Mechanical stress can cause bent pins that break off or become disconnected internally. Such stress can arise from rough handling, including being dropped on a hard floor (either the IC or the equipment it is in). Vibration can also do damage. Sensitive equipment should have rubber feet or other means of protection to keep it from being subjected to vibrations.

When an IC has failed, you should check all other ICs that have a common connection with it. A clock signal, for instance, may go to several ICs, and excessive voltage on that line may have damaged more than one of them.

On no account should an IC, let alone a printed circuit board, be unplugged or plugged in with power on. MOS and CMOS ICs are very sensitive to voltage surges, because of the extremely thin oxide on their gates.

It is possible that unreliable intermittent operation can take place even when the IC is good. This is nearly always caused by a problem with the supply voltage. Decoupling capacitors exist everywhere in most equipment, and if one becomes leaky it may pull the supply voltage down to a level where it is marginal. As a result, an IC may work properly sometimes, and at other times not, depending on the temperature.

Defects in the printed circuit board and its connections, such as cold solder joints, small fragments of metal from solder spatter, clippings of stranded wire, and so on, can cause short circuits. It is worth looking carefully for this sort of thing before condemning an IC.

Testing Digital ICs

If you specialize in digital system and computer maintenance you will probably decide it makes sense to invest in the more elaborate data analyzer and data generator mentioned in Chapter 8. They are very expensive, however; buying them can be the same as buying a car.

In a typical application, the data generator will enter a series of 8-, 16-, 32-bit, or more, parallel words into the equipment under test, and the data analyzer will display the output signals at the output port or on a particular bus. This enables you to determine if the output signals are correct, or if there is an error. The nature of the error will give you a clue to its cause.

For instance, if you were testing the arithmetic logic of a computer, you could program the data generator to input a byte of, say, 0000 0000, and keep incrementing it until it reaches 1111 1111. If you then program the arithmetic logic unit (ALU) of the computer to add each successive two bytes together, the data analyzer will quickly show if this is being done correctly.

This is only one way in which this test equipment can be used. The instruction manuals for the data analyzer and the data generator, together with the manufacturer's manual for the unit under test, give a lot of detailed information that requires time to study and analyze. Indeed, you will spend far more time on this than on the actual test. But for troubleshooting complex digital equipment there is really no better way.

However, if a data analyzer and generator are not available, there is a way you can proceed, if the equipment is not too complex. Most digital ICs are mounted on printed circuit boards, and these in many cases (especially in computers) can be plugged in and out of the main equipment. This allows you to unplug a board where you suspect a defect exists and replace it with one you know is good. If the fault then disappears, you know it has to be in the board you removed.

The defective board can then be analyzed by applying inputs simultaneously to it and to a good board in parallel with it, and noting where the outputs differ. From this, it is generally possible to determine which of the individual ICs is likely to be defective.

Comparison of individual ICs is quite simple. A clip-on device that holds a good IC is mounted over the suspect IC, and their outputs compared. However, if you do not have one of these, you can do the same thing with the test clip described in Chapter 8 and a good IC mounted on a solderless breadboard, connected pin by pin to the pins on the test clip. The inputs and outputs of both ICs can then be checked with a logic probe.

Use of the logic probe was explained in Chapter 8, so it is not necessary to repeat it here. It is possible to use an AMT or DMM where a logic probe is not available, but this method is only good for voltage levels; it will not work with pulse trains. Pulse trains can be seen on an oscilloscope, of course.

Many ICs are used today in consumer equipment. It is always best to begin troubleshooting in the external circuits around these before suspecting the IC. This is because these ICs are quite complex, and custom-made for the particular section in which they are used. Defects or faulty connections in any of the circuits around the IC can give the appearance of a defect in the IC itself. Only if you find that some of the input and output signals have deteriorated *within* the IC can you say it is indeed defective. Only an exact replacement can be used for such custom-made devices.

10

HELPFUL TIPS AND SHORTCUTS

Every trade has its tricks. By tricks we do not mean deceptive practices, but ways of doing some things that cut corners and save time. This chapter describes a few; you will devise others of your own as you develop your skills in electronics.

RADIO RECEIVER

Dead Receiver

Battery Check.   This seems so obvious that we would never have thought of including it, if it were not for the fact that it is so often overlooked. A very high proportion of radio receivers today run on batteries, and batteries run down. Therefore, the first thing to look at is the battery. It is no use taking the battery out and measuring its voltage with your AMT or DMM. You must test it *under load*. The simplest way to do this is to measure its voltage while it is connected in the radio, with the radio switched on. Its voltage should then be not less than 95 percent of its no-load voltage. If it is less, replace it. Otherwise, it will probably run down while you are performing other tests, thus complicating the problem. Alternatively, if you must test the battery out of the receiver, connect a 1-kilohm resistor across its terminals before measuring the voltage.

Click Test.   Holding the receiver close to your ear, switch it on and off. If you don't hear a click in the speaker, something has to be wrong in the speaker or its connections.

Noise Test.   Switch the receiver on and turn the volume full on. Hold it close to your ear and listen for noise. If there is none, or very little, the second detector or audio driver stage may be at fault.

Resistance Check.   Disconnect the battery, and turn the power switch on. With your DMM, measure the resistance across the battery input terminals (*not* the battery terminals). The leads should be connected with the same polarity as the battery (the red lead is usually positive, but check this if you are not sure). Allow the DMM reading to stabilize (this may take time). The measured resistance is typically 100 kilohms for AM, 4 kilohms for FM. Anything very much higher or lower would be suspicious, suggesting a problem in the power supply, or V_{cc} circuit (an "infinite" reading would probably be due to a power switch defect). If you use an AMT for this test, the FM resistance will be about the same, but the AM will be around 30 kilohms. However, the actual readings will depend upon the radios and the meters. A check with a similar radio which you know to be good will give you a reference that applies to your own instruments.

Current.   If the radio is battery powered, turn off the power and disconnect one battery terminal. Select the dc mA function on the DMM, and connect its leads between the disconnected battery and power input terminals. It should read zero current. Switch on the radio, and tune it for a spot between stations. With the volume control set to minimum, the DMM will indicate a current of a few milliamperes (a typical value might be 19 mA, but this will not be the same for all radios). Then tune a strong local station and turn the volume to maximum. If the radio is operating as it should, the current will increase considerably (probably about double what it was before). If it does not, there is something wrong, probably in the audio section.

If you can perform this test with a similar radio that is working correctly, you can compare the current values. If the "bad" radio is drawing excessive current, it would suggest leakage in an electrolytic capacitor or a transistor (this can happen if at any time the battery was installed with the wrong polarity). If the current is well below the proper level, it suggests a dead stage.

Local Oscillator.   If the local oscillator is not working, you will also have a dead receiver. A quick check of this is to place it beside another receiver that is working. Turn both radios on. Tune the good receiver to a spot between stations in the upper part of the band (1000 to 1600 kHz for AM; 98 to 108 MHz for FM), and turn its volume control to maximum. Then tune the "bad" receiver across the lower half of the band (545 to 1000 kHz for AM; 88 to 98

MHz for FM). At some point you should hear a loud noise from the "good" receiver. The noise may be a whistle, a squawk, or a burst of static. Verify that this is emanating from the bad receiver by switching it off and on. If you *don't* hear anything, its local oscillator is not working.

The local oscillator is tuned to generate a signal with a frequency of 455 kHz for AM, 10.7 MHz for FM, higher than the setting of the tuning dial. Therefore, if the bad receiver is tuned to, say, 800 kHz, its local oscillator will be generating a signal of 800 + 455 = 1255 kHz. This will be picked up at that point on the dial of the good receiver. Similarly, if a bad FM radio is tuned to, say, 88 MHz, its local oscillator will generate a signal of 88 + 10.7 = 98.7 MHz, and this will be picked up at that point on the dial of the good receiver.

However, the FM dial is very crowded, and you may have difficulty finding a blank spot between stations. In that case, tune the good radio to a spot above the upper end of the band (108 MHz); you should be able to hear the local oscillator signal here.

Audio Amplifier

The most likely thing to go wrong in a Class A audio stage is the transistor. When a transistor fails, it is usually because of a shorted or open junction. This can be verified with your DMM in accordance with Table 10-1.

TABLE 10-1   Effects on Voltages of Bad Transistor Junctions

Probable Cause	Transistor Electrode Voltages		
	Collector	Emitter	Base
Emitter shorted to base	Same as supply voltage	0	0
Emitter open	Same as supply voltage	0	Normal
Collector shorted to base	Low	High*	High
Collector open	Same as supply voltage	Normal	Normal
Base open	Same as supply voltage	0	Normal

*When there is an emitter resistor; otherwise, 0

A weak stage, in which there is more or less leakage across a junction results in below normal output. If the collector-base junction is at fault, the collector voltage will be very low, although the base and emitter voltages will be near normal. If the junction is leaking, rather than open or shorted, shorting the emitter to the base will increase the collector voltage only slightly, whereas if the transistor were good it would go to the level of the supply voltage. This test should be applied to the transistor in each of the cases given in the table, after the voltage measurement. If the transistor is good, you will also hear a click from the speaker. Then, if the voltages are still incorrect, the fault must be somewhere other than in the transistor.

If shorting the base to the emitter cannot be done for some reason, you can try connecting a 100-kilohm resistor between the base and the battery positive terminal (negative terminal if the transistor is PNP). If the transistor is good, the collector voltage should decrease. However, if it does not change, the transistor is not necessarily bad; the fault could be elsewhere.

Speaker Phasing.   When connecting two speakers you need to get them in phase with each other, otherwise the bass response will be unsatisfactory. If the terminals are not marked, you can still do this by reversing the connections of one speaker, and seeing which way gives the best response.

Pop Check to Isolate Bad Stage

To find the stage where the signal is blocked, touch a screwdriver, with your finger in contact with its blade, to the input of each stage in turn, starting with the last. There should be a "pop" each time. If you do not hear a pop at the input of a stage, that stage is not working. The pops should get louder as you go from the later to the earlier stages.

MOBILE RADIO

The following checks are not a substitute for internal adjustments that affect compliance with FCC rules. They require no more than simple homemade test gear (some need none at all). It is essential, however, that you use a dummy antenna when operating a transmitter, and also that you do not operate it for extended lengths of time before checking that the standing-wave ratio (SWR) is under 3 to 1.

Dummy Antenna

A simple dummy antenna that can be made from a #47 miniature lamp and a PL-259 plug is shown in Figure 10–1. This lamp has a dc resistance of 42 ohms, which is close enough to the usual 50-ohm coaxial line and antenna impedance for practical purposes. It is plugged into the transceiver's output jack, and enables you to check relative power output and modulation.

Antenna Test

For this test all you need is a 12- or 14-volt auto lamp, such as a #1815, a bayonet-type lamp socket, and two 10-foot lengths of insulated wire, each with an alligator clip on one end. The other ends are soldered to the terminals of the lamp socket.

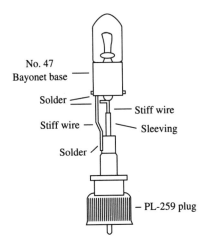

No. 47
Bayonet base

Solder

Stiff wire

Stiff wire

Sleeving

Solder

PL-259 plug

Figure 10–1 Dummy Antenna

Disconnect the antenna coaxial lead from the transceiver output jack. Then connect one alligator clip to the antenna and the other to the positive terminal of the car battery (assuming a negative ground). With a screwdriver, short together the center pin and outside shell of the coaxial connector. The lamp should light.

The lamp might light *before* you short the coaxial terminal. If this happens, you may have a shunt-fed, base-loaded antenna. Look for a loading coil in the whip. Obviously, this test doesn't work with that type of antenna. However, if this is not the case, then you must have a short in the antenna system. The coaxial connectors are usually to blame.

AM Modulation Check

You can use the dummy antenna described previously to check the modulation of an AM transceiver. Disconnect the antenna, connect the dummy antenna in its place (at the output of the transceiver), and energize the transceiver. The lamp will light. Note the brilliance of the lamp as you speak into the microphone. If the carrier is being modulated, the brightness of the lamp will vary in accordance with the loudness of your voice. This method does not give you the percentage of modulation, but does show that modulation is taking place.

Carrier Frequency Check

This check can be done if you have available a multiband receiver with an S-meter. Substitute the dummy antenna for the external one, and energize the transceiver and multiband receiver. If the receiver has a built-in calibrator, calibrate it. After an adequate warm-up period, energize the transmitter and tune the receiver for peak deflection of the S-meter. However, distance the transmitter and receiver from each other so that the S-meter is not overloaded. Read the transmitter frequency from the receiver tuning dial. This check does *not* meet FCC calibration requirements, of course.

Audio Stage Check

If you performed the modulation check described previously, you do not need to check the audio again, since it was done in that check (transceivers generally use the same stage for modulation).

Audio Power Output Check

You need to know the rated audio power output for the transceiver (given in the operator's manual). Begin by disconnecting the speaker output lead from the transceiver and substituting a resistor with a resistance equal to the speaker impedance. This resistor should also be capable of absorbing the maximum power that will be applied to it. Connect your DMM across the resistor, and turn on the receiver. Turn the squelch control off and the volume control full on.

The voltage across the resistor will be in accordance with the formula

$$V = \sqrt{PR}$$

where V is the rms voltage measured by the DMM, P is the rated power output, and R is the value of the resistor. Table 10-2 gives the voltages corresponding to various values of P for a resistance of 8 ohms (a common speaker impedance value). However, you will have to use your calculator for other resistances.

TABLE 10-2   Voltages to Be Expected with an 8-Ohm Resistance

Rated Power Output (watts)	Voltage Read on DMM (V_{rms})
0.5	2.0
1	2.8
2	4.0
3	4.9
4	5.7
5	6.3

Power Input Check

If your transceiver does not seem to be getting power, a simple check is to disconnect its normal input power connection and connect it directly to the car battery. If it fails to function this way, the fault must lie in the set. Otherwise, the problem must be in the power cable, plug, or fuse.

If it seems that the fault lies in the set, disconnect it from the battery, or other power supply, discharge the filter capacitors, and measure the resistance across the power input leads (with the power switch turned on). A low resistance is good; a high resistance indicates trouble in the internal power supply.

In the case of a base station, unplug the power cord from the utility outlet, and measure the resistance across the power plug pins. A low resistance is good, so check the utility outlet for 120 V_{rms}. A high resistance indicates trouble in the internal power supply.

VIDEO CASSETTE RECORDER

There is not much you can do in the way of shortcuts, but if you expect to service VCRs frequently you should make yourself an alignment tape. Most manufacturers recommend tools and tapes that you can get from them. However, these are designed for their own product, and you want something that you can use with any VCR. To make such a tape, get a blank cassette and record on it the color bars transmitted by a local TV station. These are usually transmitted early in the morning, before regular programming begins, or late at night, after it ceases.

Basic VCR Check

When checking a VCR, first make sure that the fine tuning of the TV channel (3 or 4) used with the VCR in the TV receiver is properly adjusted. Play your alignment cassette, and get the best color bar display possible. Then check to make sure the VCR fine tuning is also correctly adjusted.

If the picture is unsatisfactory, switch to TV, and check the picture quality of each TV channel, using the TV receiver's channel selector. This will show you if there is a problem with the TV receiver, such as defective antenna connections, internal troubles, or tuning troubles.

If reception by the TV is satisfactory, switch to VCR, and reset the TV receiver to channel 3 or 4, whichever it is using for VCR. With the VCR channel selector, check the performance of each VCR channel.

If the picture quality is bad, or there is no picture at all on all VCR channels, recheck the adjustment of the fine tuning on channel 3 or 4 on the TV receiver. If only certain channels are affected, check the VCR fine tuning.

If the picture quality is good while displaying a broadcast program through the VCR, record a portion of it, then play it back. If the replay is not good, then suspect the video heads of the VCR.

AUDIO CASSETTE RECORDERS

Most audio tape recorders are cassette recorders. The best way to service them is to obtain (from an electronic parts store) a cassette made for that purpose, which cleans and demagnetizes the tape head and tape handling parts in one step.

Flutter and Wow Check

Use a blank tape to record a 3-kHz tone. This can be derived from an audio signal generator driving a speaker. Then play it back, listening carefully. If objectionable flutter or wow are present you will hear it (the human ear can detect speed variations as low as 0.1 percent). Many cassette recorders have speed variations of over 0.5 percent even when new, so that small amounts that would not be noticeable to the average listener are tolerable.

Head Magnetization Check

Use a blank cassette. Connect your DMM to the recorder output jack (earphone jack). Short the input circuit (a shorted phone plug will do this if there is a microphone input jack). Run the cassette for a short time, and note the reading on the DMM. Rewind the tape and play it again. Do not change the settings of any controls. Note the reading on the DMM during the replay. If there is a difference between the first and second readings, one of the heads (if there is more than one) is magnetized. However, do this several times to be sure; if the difference persists, demagnetization is required.

MONOCHROME TELEVISION RECEIVER

TV receivers, especially modern ones, are very complex, relying heavily on ICs. When faced with one that is giving trouble, you can save considerable time by careful evaluation of the trouble symptoms. Follow the procedure outlined in Chapter 1 (questions you might ask the owner of the equipment to find out what happened). Then try all the receiver's controls to see if there is any response; it doesn't matter how bad the response is, *anything* will help you get an idea of what is wrong.

If there is snow on the screen, turn the contrast control to maximum. Try different channels. A high snow level indicates a fault in the front end.

Remove the back of the receiver cabinet, and see if there is anything visible, audible, or smellable going on. Technicians call this the smoke test. If the owner mentioned a snapping sound or a smell of burning varnish, you might expect to find that something, such as a resistor, has cremated itself. (If

the inside of the cabinet is very dirty, it is a good idea to clean it first; you may
spot the problem while you are doing this.)

Also check that all cables, plugs, and jacks are properly connected; this
includes external cables to the VCR, and so on. Some other quick checks that
do not require removing the TV receiver's cabinet are given below.

Power Supply Input Resistance

Unplug the power cord. Measure the input resistance of the power supply
across the pins of the power plug. A small black-and-white receiver typically
will have a resistance of 40 ohms. This is the dc resistance of the power
transformer primary winding. Obviously, a very high resistance would indicate
it was open (assuming the power switch is on). In this case, there would have
been nothing on the screen when the power was on.

Local Oscillator Check

If there is heavy snow on the screen, there is a distinct possibility that the
local oscillator in the tuner is not functioning. You can verify this by feeding an
unmodulated signal via a 1-kilohm resistor to the antenna input with a
frequency of 99.5 MHz (channel 2 local oscillator frequency). While watching
the screen, vary the tuning of the signal generator around 99.5 MHz. If the
picture reappears, even if only momentarily, it is likely that there is a problem
in the local oscillator circuit.

High Voltage Check

If there is sound but no picture, there may be a defect in the high voltage
section, or the picture tube may be dead. You can check this quickly with a
pocket radio. Turn on the TV and the radio, and hold the radio close to the TV
screen. Tune the radio across the AM band. Starting at 535.5 kHz, the radio
should squawk, whistle, or give some such indication every 15.75 kHz if it is
picking up the horizontal sweep (which will be absent if the high voltage section
is defective). If the 15.75 kHz signal is present, you should then check the
picture tube.

The picture tube itself may not be bad; the trouble could be in the
voltages applied to it. To check these, unplug the picture tube socket, and
measure the voltage on each pin, comparing these with the manufacturer's
schematic diagram. If they are all within specification, it looks like you need a
new tube. However, you may wish to make a further check of the high voltage,
for which all you need is a neon bulb. Attach it to a wooden dowel, or other
insulated rod, with electrical tape, and hold it near a high voltage point. If high
voltage is present, the bulb will glow.

11

TROUBLESHOOTING INTERMITTENT DEFECTS AND INTERFERENCE

INTERMITTENT DEFECTS

An intermittent defect is caused by the random opening and closing of an electrical connection somewhere in a piece of electronic equipment. This may be causing a short circuit to ground, or to some other circuit, or it may be interrupting the flow of power or signal currents. Although the effect is electrical, the cause is not. There are, in fact, two causes that account for practically all intermittent problems. One is mechanical, the other thermal.

MECHANICAL CAUSES

Mechanical causes include vibration, shock, position, air flow, and the like. These will make loose connections act up. Such loose connections can be loose or badly fitting connector contacts, bad solder joints, broken wires, defective insulation, internal defects in ICs, transistors, or diodes, and so on.

How to Locate a Mechanical Intermittent

The first thing to do is to verify that the defect is indeed mechanical. You do this by shaking or thumping the entire thing to see if this causes the intermittent defect to appear or disappear. If it does, obviously the cause is mechanical.

The nature of the defect should give you a clue as to where in the equipment to start looking for the cause of the problem. This involves removing the chassis from its cabinet. When you have done this, and with the power off, turn the chassis upside down, and shake it to see if anything falls out. This should be done over a clean surface, so that if anything does drop out, you can see it. The reason for doing this is that a small piece of metal, such as wire or solder, may be in there. However, a lot of dust and dirt may also fall out, but you can usually spot a piece of metal quite easily. If the equipment is very dirty, the dust and dirt should be blown out first, using an air compressor, if one is available, or a spray can of compressed air that you can get from an electronic parts store. In this way you can direct the air under components and wires where a piece of metal might be hiding, so that it will more readily fall out when you turn the chassis upside down. After doing this, turn the power back on, to see if the intermittent defect is still there. It may be necessary to thump the chassis again to make it misbehave.

The next step is a visual inspection of the suspected section of the equipment. You are looking for any discoloration, especially burn marks, melted wax, damaged insulation, and so on. If you don't see anything, turn the power back on, and try to locate the trouble by bending, prodding, tapping, or jiggling wires, terminals, and components. You need a "wiggler" for this. A wiggler is a short plastic or wooden rod about 10 inches long and a quarter of an inch in diameter (these dimensions are approximate, of course), with a slot cut in one end, as shown in Figure 11-1. In this way, when this causes the intermittent fault to become permanent as you jiggle something, you will know you have found its location.

Figure 11-1 Wiggler

Intermittents on printed circuit boards most often arise from a hairline crack that causes an open circuit, a short between adjacent conductors, or a defective plated-through hole. The hardest to find is the hairline crack, since it is almost invisible. The best way to find it is to jumper all suspected conductors by connecting pieces of insulated wire between the ends of each, and turning the power back on. If that restores proper performance, it must be one of the jumpered conductors. The repair would be to solder the jumper in place.

A short between conductors may be caused by a hair-thin wire, a piece of solder, or something else bridging the gap between two conductors. A magnifying glass is helpful here. You can also slide a toothpick, or something similar, between the adjacent conductors, where they are close together, and see whether this clears the short.

If the problem is a defective plated-through hole, you have a tough job, because the break will be inside, where you can't see it. Don't start by looking for a defective plated-through hole. Look for a cracked conductor first. If you have eliminated that possibility, the simplest solution to the plated-through hole problem is to resolder all plated-through hole connections on both sides. The wire lead going through the plated hole will then provide the connection, instead of the defective plated hole.

If you are doing any soldering on a printed circuit board, don't use a heavy-duty soldering iron. A 15- or 25-watt pencil-type is strong enough and won't damage the board. Make sure the solder flows smoothly, and do not move the parts being soldered while the solder is setting. Don't try to hurry the setting process by touching it with a cold screwdriver; let it harden by itself. If you are adding solder, be sure and use the rosin-core type.

Don't forget to check all connectors that might be involved. They are responsible for more intermittents than any other component. Again, bridging the suspected plug and jack portion of a multipin connector is the best way to locate the defect.

THERMAL CAUSES

Since metal expands and contracts with changes of temperature, and since most connections are metallic, a poor contact is likely to be pulled apart or pushed together as equipment warms or cools.

How to Locate a Thermal Intermittent

One of the best ways of finding an intermittent defect that is due to temperature change is to "freeze" the printed circuit board or other suspected portion of the circuit where you think it may be. You can get a can of "instant freeze" from an electronic parts store. This will have an extender tube so that you can spray any desired spot. Be careful to keep the spray off any component that is susceptible to damage from cold, such as semiconductors.

Alternatively, you can apply heat from a hair dryer. This would be your choice if the defect is one that appears after a lengthy warm-up period. The same caution about care with semiconductors applies to heating them, especially germanium types.

Sometimes a stubborn intermittent refuses to respond to either the mechanical method or the thermal method of locating it. You should then try both together. You can do this by wrapping the offending device in a thick towel, letting it get really warm, and then subjecting it to thumping or shaking as you did for a mechanical defect. If this doesn't bring on the intermittent defect, nothing will. However, the way you go about this will depend upon the type of equipment you are troubleshooting. Some items might be too large or have other complications that would need different handling.

INTERFERENCE DEFECTS

Interference is any kind of unwanted signal that spoils the operation of some piece of electronic gear you are using. It can be external (originating outside the equipment) or internal (originating inside the equipment). External interference includes amateur radio transmitters, computer operation, microwave oven operation, ac hum, and so on. Internal interference is frequently ac hum arising in the power supply, or noise in the tuner when the incoming signal is too weak.

The first thing you have to do is identify the interference. Is it always there, or from time to time? If it is always there, it is most likely internal. If it comes on occasionally, it is more likely to be external. A quick way of verifying this in the case of a receiver is to short the antenna terminals together, or to ground. Of course, the signal being received will disappear, but if the interference remains it must be originating internally. However, while the antenna is still shorted, turn the receiver to face in various directions. If the interference becomes weaker or stronger when you do this, it must be external after all, but it is being picked up by the internal wiring. A further step to verify this, if possible, would be to move the receiver to a place, such as a concrete basement, where it would be shielded from outside interference, and see if this gets rid of it.

If the interference is in the form of 60-Hz ac hum, you may suspect that it is entering through the ac power line. This can be checked by connecting a 0.1-μF capacitor with a voltage rating of not less that 400 V_{dc} across the power line where it enters the equipment, to see if this reduces it.

External Interference

Every electromagnetic signal that impinges on a receiver's antenna induces a current in it that appears at the antenna input terminals. It is the tuner's job to select only the one you want. So how does an unwanted signal get through?

Heterodyning

Although the interfering signal may be of a different frequency from that of the desired signal, it may still give rise to another frequency by *heterodyning,* and this frequency may be one to which some part of the equipment is sensitive. Heterodyning occurs when the unwanted signal and the wanted signal are mixed in a nonlinear impedance. A nonlinear impedance can be a diode, a transistor, a vacuum tube, or even a defective solder joint. The two input signals beat together to produce four output signals, which consist of the original two signals, a third made up of the sum of the frequencies of the original two, and a fourth made up of the difference of the frequencies of the original two. For instance, if the two incoming signals have frequencies of 1.0 MHz and 0.75 MHz, the four output signals will have frequencies of 1.0, 0.75, (1.0 + 0.75), and (1.0 − 0.75) MHz.

These four frequencies are fundamental frequencies. Each fundamental frequency also generates harmonics, and although these are weaker, one may happen to have a frequency that allows it to be picked up by some part of the equipment. For example, the IF frequency band of a TV receiver is from 41.25 to 45.75 MHz. It would be sensitive to the sixth harmonic (42 MHz) of a transmitter operating at 7 MHz, assuming the transmitter was emitting harmonics and was close by.

When you encounter this type of interference, you may be able to identify the owner of the device causing it. A radio amateur, for instance, could be recognized by the streaks appearing in the TV picture when he is on the air. You may also hear his voice, and from that you will get his call sign (unless he is using code, of course). He is probably unaware that he is causing interference, and will be glad to correct it. However, if you cannot identify the source, you can also contact the regional office of the Federal Communications Commission (FCC) for help.

Signals that are of one frequency, such as this example, can be eliminated by installing a suitable filter. This consists of a circuit resonant at the undesired frequency. Figure 11–2 shows a series-resonant circuit that you connect across the signal input (the antenna terminals). At the undesired frequency, to which it is tuned, it shunts the input as if the terminals had been shorted together. The equation for calculating the values of the inductor and capacitor is

$$LC = \frac{1}{(2\pi f)^2} \, .$$

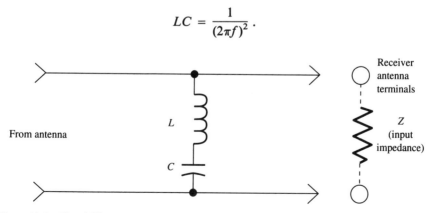

Figure 11–2 Signal Filter

However, if there is more than one interfering signal, it may be better to use a high-pass filter, which will attenuate all frequencies that are lower than the lowest signal you want to receive. Such a filter is shown in Figure 11–3. In this case you need to take into consideration the input impedance of the receiver. In the case of a TV receiver you would want to block all signals below 50 MHz, so this would be the cutoff frequency f_c. The values of L and C are given by

$$L = \frac{Z}{4\pi f_c} \quad \text{and} \quad C = \frac{1}{2\pi f_c Z}.$$

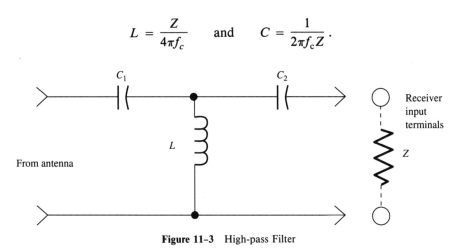

Figure 11–3   High-pass Filter

Assuming the input impedance Z is 75 Ω, the value of the capacitor is given by

$$C = \frac{1}{2 \times \pi \times 50 \times 10^6 \times 75}$$

$$= 42 \text{ pF.}$$

(You can parallel capacitors to get the exact value required.)
And the value of the inductance is given by

$$L = \frac{75}{4 \times \pi \times 50 \times 10^6}$$

$$= 0.119 \ \mu\text{H.}$$

A coil of that value would not be available "off the shelf," so it would be necessary to make one. If it is wound on a coil form with a diameter of 0.5 inch and length 1 inch, the number of turns is given by

$$N = \frac{[L(9r + 10l)]^{1/2}}{r}$$

where N = the number of turns, L = the inductance in microhenries, r = the radius of the coil, and l its length. In this case, the radius is 0.25 inch and the length 1.0 inch. The required inductance is 0.119 μH.

$$N = \frac{[0.119(9 \times 0.25 + 10 \times 1.0)]^{1/2}}{0.25}$$

$$\cong 5 \text{ turns}$$

This filter is installed across the input terminals, with the capacitors in series with the center conductor of the coaxial transmission line from the antenna.

In the less likely event that interference is coming from a signal with a higher frequency than the one you wish to receive, you will need a low-pass filter, as shown in Figure 11-4. The equations for this filter are

$$L = \frac{Z}{f_c} \quad \text{and} \quad C = \frac{1}{f_c Z}.$$

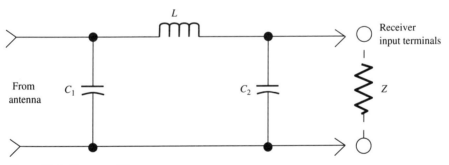

Figure 11-4 Low-pass Filter

You make the coil in the same way as described above for the high-pass filter.

Noise

An example of noise is the interference that appears on a TV screen as a snowstorm of "colored snow." It is either external or internal, but usually doesn't appear when a strong signal is being received. In the case where the signal is weak or absent, the automatic gain control increases the gain to maximum, and in so doing amplifies the noise.

Noise originating at the front end of the receiver gets more amplification than that originating in later stages, so as a general rule we would look in the tuner for an internal noise source caused by random motion of electrons in a resistor or other component.

If there is no station operating on the TV channel, or if a radio receiver is tuned between stations, noise is normal. However, if there should be a signal, then there is a problem with the tuner or the antenna, since the signal is not being received. A weaker noise indication might mean that the signal is being interrupted after the tuner, and therefore being amplified less.

External noise is usually manmade. A common source is from automobile ignition. Spark plug leads are supposed to be resistive, to suppress interference of this sort, but if some backyard mechanic has replaced one with a length of ordinary insulated wire, he will be broadcasting all over the neighborhood every time he drives down the street.

Household appliances also produce noise, although this type of noise will probably enter through the power line, since your TV receiver, radio, and so on, are on the same power distribution circuit as the vacuum cleaner, food processor, or whatever is being used at the time.

External noise that is not manmade is sometimes picked up. The most common is caused by electrical storms, so it is of a temporary nature. Other sources include noise from the Sun when sunspots are very bad. Noise from Jupiter and galactic noise are seldom bad enough to be noticeable.

The main difference between random noise and heterodyne interference is that noise has no fixed frequency, so you can't get rid of it by filtering. The only way you can reduce noise is by shielding. Most equipment is shielded from internal noise, but external noise may be picked up by the antenna or transmission line.

Many external antennas, especially TV antennas, are directional, so that the antenna can be oriented to weaken the noise pickup, if that doesn't weaken the signal too much also. Fortunately, a great deal of noise is strongest near to the ground, so that raising the elevation of the antenna may be the best solution. Also, using a shielded transmission line will make a big improvement. You still see many TV antennas connected to their receivers with twin lead transmission line. This picks up all kinds of interference. Where it is taped to metal objects it picks up even more, as well as attenuating the signal. If you have a noise problem, and the transmission line is 300-ohm twin lead, you should change it for 75-ohm coaxial line, terminated at each end with 75- to 300-ohm impedance matching transformers.

Many modern receivers have a 75-ohm input impedance with coaxial connectors, but if the old 300-ohm antenna and transmission line are going to be used, abundant snow will be created by the resulting mismatch. Instead of getting a 300- to 75-ohm adapter for the receiver input, you'd do much better to install a 75-ohm transmission line with an adapter at the antenna. Consider getting a new antenna also.

In cases where an antenna is not involved, as in an audio setup, and there is severe noise interference that you cannot get at, you may have to try moving the equipment to another location. If that doesn't work, you can try constructing a cage of fine wire mesh (fly screen, for instance). The wire cage should stand on a plate of metal, and be bonded to it. This cage should be grounded to a good ground, and the audio equipment must be insulated from it. In this way, the interference will be picked up by the cage and grounded instead of entering the equipment. It will probably be necessary to shield the power cord also, using a shielded cable such as BX, and grounding the power line itself for RF by connecting a capacitor between it and the cage.

Grounding

As mentioned above, a shield, to be effective, must be properly grounded. This means connection to the Earth itself via a low-resistance path. The best ground consists of a copper rod at least eight feet long, driven into moist soil, and connected to the chassis or shield to be grounded by a thick copper conductor (braid or heavy wire) by the shortest possible route. Such ground rods are often provided with a drip supply of water to maintain the soil's moisture in dry weather. However, for most purposes, connection to a water pipe, provided it is metal, will achieve an adequate result.

Before making such a connection, you must be certain that the chassis of the equipment is not "hot." This means that it is not connected in any way to the power line. Isolation from the ac line is usually provided by a power transformer, but if the equipment power supply does not use one (as was common practice in sets using vacuum tubes), an isolation 1:1 transformer may be required.

Generally speaking, noise is present everywhere, all the time, but if the signal-to-noise ratio is good it will not be a problem as a rule. Anything that weakens the signal (poor antenna and transmission line, distance from station, and so on), or any strong source of noise nearby, that competes with the signal, may have to be corrected. Your remedy will depend upon the cause of the interference.

12

HOW ACCURATE IS YOUR TEST EQUIPMENT?

How do you know that the reading of a test instrument is the real value of the quantity you are measuring? When you buy it, you assume that the manufacturer's specification gives an honest statement of its capabilities, but does it stay that way? After it has been in use for some time, does it still have the same accuracy? Are its indications still true?

If you own expensive instruments, and their continual accuracy is important, you can send them at regular intervals to a calibration laboratory, where they are compared to the laboratory standard instruments that are much more accurate. If necessary, they are adjusted to bring them back to their original specifications. The laboratory standards themselves are calibrated at regular intervals against even more accurate standards.

The ultimate standards are unvarying physical quantities. For instance, time (and frequency) are referenced to the quantum mechanics of the cesium-133 atom. The kilogram is the mass of a cylinder of platinum-iridium alloy kept by the International Bureau of Standards in Paris. The length of the meter is defined as 1 650 763.73 wavelengths in a vacuum of the orange-red line of the spectrum of krypton-86. From these and other *base units* the precise values of all units are derived.

In the United States, the National Bureau of Standards has the responsibility for maintaining *primary standards* that enable comparisons to be made with these unvarying physical quantities. At the next lower level, government and other agencies have calibration centers that provide a link between the NBS primary standards and the *working standards* that calibrate test equipment used at the workshop or flight-line level. These intermediate standards are called *secondary standards*. They are sent to NBS periodically for recalibration against primary standards. Although they are less accurate than NBS standards, secondary standards nevertheless are extremely sensitive instruments that must be maintained in a special environment and handled with great care. At the shop level, the working standards that are used to perform periodical calibration of test equipment used in engineering research or product control go at intervals to be recalibrated against the secondary standards.

In this way, performance or other data measured during proof-testing of factory products, servicing of radio equipment, and so on, are traceable back to the basic physical quantities via a test equipment pyramid in which each level is more accurate than the one beneath it, as Figure 12–1 shows.

But what about the "ordinary" test equipment that most of us have? In theory it should be recalibrated at intervals, but it seldom is. So how can you verify that it is still as accurate as it is supposed to be?

There are a few "standards" you can use that are readily available. For a voltage standard you can use a fresh, unused alkaline D cell, which should have a value of 1.56 V_{dc}. For frequency, you can use the power line, which gives 60 ±0.01 Hz. As long as the "standard" you use is four or five times as accurate as the instrument you are calibrating, it will do. This should be done every year, and the date should be noted.

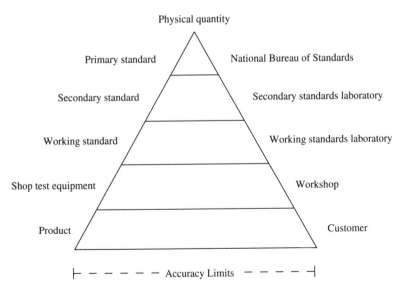

Figure 12–1   Test Equipment Accuracy Pyramid

VOLTAGE CALIBRATION

DC Voltage Calibration

As mentioned above, an ordinary alkaline D cell, when fresh and unused, has a voltage of 1.56 V_{dc}, so one can be used for a voltage standard. Such a cell will give a reading of 1.56 V_{dc} on a DMM, but may read only 1.3 V_{dc} on a 2,000 ohms per volt AMT due to loading. Once it is put into use, the voltage begins to decline, and from then on it gradually decreases until it is used up.

For example, assume that the lowest dc range of your AMT is 0–3 V_{dc}. First, make sure the pointer is over the zero mark. Use the mirror scale (if there isn't one, position your eye directly above the pointer) to get the pointer, its reflection, and the zero mark in line. If the pointer is not over the zero mark, use a small screwdriver to rotate the zero adjustment located below the dial so that the pointer first moves upscale. Then continue rotation in the same direction until it comes back down over the zero mark. Tap the AMT gently to make sure it is exactly over the mark.

Now connect the leads to the flashlight cell, with the proper polarity so that the pointer is not driven down against the limit pin. A 20,000 ohms per volt meter should now indicate close to 1.56 V_{dc} on the 0–3 V_{dc} range scale. However, bear in mind that the accuracy of the AMT on dc may be, say, ± 3.0 percent of full scale. On this scale, where the full-scale value is 3 V_{dc}, that will be ± 0.09 V_{dc}, so the reading will be within specification if it is anywhere between 1.47 and 1.65 V_{dc}. Do not readjust the zero adjustment to set the pointer to 1.56 V_{dc}, since small inaccuracies of the range resistors may make it worse on other ranges. These figures will be different for your meter, unless it has a 0–3 V_{dc} scale and an accuracy of ± 3.0 percent.

If you are doing this with a DMM, your accuracy will be greater, say, ± 1.0 percent of reading. This will mean that your reading should be between 1.54 and 1.58 V_{dc}. If the accuracy is even greater, ± 0.1 percent for example, you should expect an exact reading.

These tests show you whether the instrument is performing as it should on one range only. It does tell you that the meter movement or digital circuits are working as they should. But for the higher ranges, you will have to rely upon the accuracy of the range resistors. If there is reason to think that a particular range may be off, but calibration showed the lowest range to be within tolerance, you should suspect a damaged range resistor. If the manufacturer's manual gives directions for returning the meter for repair, follow those rather than trying to do it yourself. In many cases, you should weigh the advantages of buying a new meter against the cost of repairs, postage, and so on, since this may be a better option.

AC Voltage Calibration

With some voltmeters you can use the D cell as above on the ac range. With one type, the reading will be zero with one polarity and twice the voltage (3.12 V_{dc}) with the other. With another type, the reading will be zero with one polarity and 1.56 V_{dc} with the other. Where this won't work, the only way you can do it is to use the line voltage and another ac voltmeter that you know to be accurate. Using the proper precautions, connect the two voltmeters in parallel, set to read ac volts, and compare their readings.

Resistance and Current Functions

To test these functions, you should get a precision resistor (at least ± 1 percent) from the local electronics parts store, otherwise you will have a Catch-22 situation. With a precision resistor you will be able to measure resistance within the accuracy of the resistor. This is close enough for most purposes, and the same applies to the current you measure flowing through it, using the circuit shown in Figure 12-2. This current should agree with the value obtained from $I = V/R$.

Oscilloscope

The calibration voltage output terminal of an oscilloscope typically provides a square wave of 1 kHz with an amplitude of 0.5 V_{p-p}. This is generated by a multivibrator powered by a regulated V_{cc}, and is very stable. It can be used for checking the performance of the other circuits.

To verify the accuracy of the vertical amplifier, first set the input switch to DC and the probe to 1:1 attenuation. Then connect it to the calibration signal output terminal. Set the triggering level control to AUTO. Set the

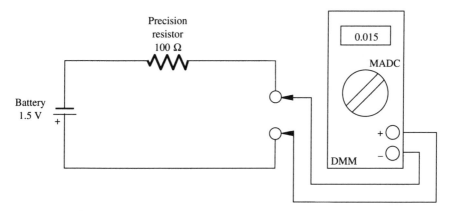

Figure 12-2   Measuring Current with a Precision Resistor

VOLTS/DIV variable control to its calibrated (detent) position, and adjust the VOLTS/DIV and SWEEP TIME/DIV controls for a stable display of convenient size (VOLTS/DIV control to 0.1 V, SWEEP TIME/DIV control to 0.2 ms per division). With the VOLTS/DIV control set to 0.1 V per division, the 0.5 V_{p-p} waveform should take up five vertical divisions of the graticule. With the vertical position control, align the lower edge of the waveform with one of the lower graticule lines (not the bottom one). With the horizontal position control, move the waveform laterally so that its upper edge cuts the vertical center line of the graticule. Then read the actual amplitude of the square wave against the scale. Assuming the calibrator signal is 0.5 V_{p-p} and the VOLTS/DIV control is set to 0.1 V per division, the square wave should measure exactly five divisions. However, allowance should be made for the accuracy specified for the vertical attenuator. If this is, say, ±3 percent, then the displayed square wave can have an amplitude between 0.485 and 0.515 V_{p-p}, or in this example, between 4.85 and 5.15 divisions of the graticule without being out of tolerance. Now set the input switch to AC; the waveform will change position vertically, but on being repositioned to where it was before, you should see no change in amplitude. If your scope has two vertical input amplifiers, repeat this procedure for the other amplifier.

The procedure for checking the time base is similar. Verify that the SWEEP TIME/DIV variable control is in its calibrated (detent) position, and set the SWEEP TIME/DIV control to 0.2 ms per division. The waveform will now occupy five graticule divisions horizontally. Align the left-hand side of the pulse with the second vertical graticule line from the left, and measure the duration of the pulse from this point to the left-hand side of the following pulse. It should be five divisions, but, again, if the accuracy of the time base is given as, say, ±3 percent, it could be anywhere between 4.85 and 5.15 divisions without being out of tolerance.

The procedures given above will serve to verify that these sections of the scope are functioning with their specified accuracy, provided that the calibrator signal itself is more accurate. You should, therefore, check the scope's specifications to see what the calibrator's accuracy is. If its accuracy turns out to be no better than that of the sections tested, you have not done a real calibration, although you have confirmation that your scope is probably in good order. But if you want absolute confirmation, you can verify the vertical amplifier's accuracy using the D cell method described for voltage calibration. If you do this, you must set the input to DC, of course, and the VOLTS/DIV control to 0.5 V per division. Then before applying the voltage of the D cell, align the free-running trace to the second or third horizontal graticule line. When the D cell is connected, the trace will shift upward about three divisions. The actual value read should be 1.56 ± 0.0468 V_p.

To make an accurate calibration of the time base, you will need a pulse generator with an accuracy four or five times as great as the accuracy of the time base. The best instrument, designed especially for this purpose, is a *time mark generator.* This produces sharp spikes on the screen, like the teeth of a comb, which are aligned with the graticule lines to verify the timing. However, a pulse generator will do a good job if you use the leading edge of each pulse in the same way.

If any of the above procedures indicate that readjustment is required to bring the instrument back into tolerance, you should first be sure that you know it *is* out of tolerance, and then you should follow the calibration procedure given in your manual. The steps for this procedure are intended to be done in the proper order so that subsequent adjustments will not misadjust previous ones. The adjustments are internal, necessitating removal of the scope cabinet. This means that you will need to exercise care, since the CRT will have a high voltage (typically 6,000 V_{dc}) between the cathode and the anode. It is not fatal to a person in normal health, but it is certainly nasty, and can cause you to injure yourself or the equipment by your sudden reaction. (The effect is similar to what you would get from a spark plug lead.)

Always check power supply voltages before starting calibration, since the proper operation of many circuits depends on them.

PREVENTIVE MAINTENANCE

Apart from calibration, test equipment requires periodic cleaning and removal of accumulations of dirt. Dirt and debris in the interior can be blown out with compressed air, if available. If not, then brushing with a soft brush, combined with turning the chassis upside down and shaking it, will get rid of the loose stuff. Obviously you do this after removing the cabinet. Do not be so vigorous that you cause damage to wiring or printed circuit boards. Pay particular attention to connectors, plugs, and jacks, since these are a frequent source of problems.

The outside of the cabinet can be cleaned with a soft cloth, if necessary moistened with a diluted household cleaning solution. Be careful not to use something that is strong enough to erase the panel markings or remove the paint. Many plastic materials are susceptible to damage in this way, and the "glass" over some dials may be plastic that will become cloudy and ruined when treated with a detergent. In fact, some plastics used in this way will be scratched even by a handkerchief, so be careful. When using a damp cloth, make sure it is not excessively damp, so that water squeezed out does not run into places where it can do harm.

Always cover the equipment when it is not in use.

GLOSSARY

ac See *alternating current.*

active filter Filter employing one or more operational amplifiers.

ADC See *analog-to-digital converter.*

alternating current (ac) Electric current that surges back and forth at a steady rate, its amplitude varying in proportion to the sine of an angle that is a linear function of time. If V_{pk} is the amplitude of the sine wave, then $V_{pk}/\sqrt{2} = 0.707\,V_{pk} = V_{rms}$. 1 V_{rms} (root-mean-square) has the same effective value as 1 V_{dc}. See *root-mean-square* and *average voltage or current.*

ampere (A) That constant current which, if maintained in two straight parallel conductors of infinite length and of negligible cross section, and placed 1 meter apart in a vacuum, would produce, between these conductors, a force equal to 2×10^{-7} newton per meter of length. [A newton (1 N) is the force which, when applied to a body having a mass of 1 kilogram, causes an acceleration of 1 meter per second per second in the direction of application of the force. 1 N = 0.224809 1bf.]

analog circuit Circuit in which the electrical signals vary continuously in proportion to changes in a physical variable.

analog multitester (AMT) Instrument that measures dc volts, ac volts, ohms, and dc milliamperes, and displays the values by means of a pointer and a scale on a dial. Some AMTs have additional functions. Also called a *volt-ohm-milliammeter (VOM).*

analog-to-digital converter (ADC) Device to convert analog signals to digital form.

AND gate Logic gate in which the output is high if both inputs are high: $A \cdot B = Q.$

antilog amplifier Operational amplifier whose output is the antilog of its input.

average voltage or current The sum of the instantaneous values of voltage or current in a half-cycle waveform, divided by the number of instantaneous values. In a sine wave, V_{av} (or I_{av}) $= 0.637\,V_{pk}$ (or I_{pk}).

binary number code Number system with a base of 2, having the symbols 1 and 0.

bipolar junction transistor (BJT) Transistor with two junctions and conduction by both majority and minority carriers.

BJT See *bipolar junction transistor.*

breadboard, solderless Device for experimental layout of electronic circuits without soldering.

bus Path along which data, addresses, or control signals are transmitted or received.

capacitance The ratio between the amount of electric charge that has been transferred from one electrode of a capacitor to the other, divided by their difference of potential, given by $C = Q/V$, where C is in farads, Q in coulombs, and V in volts.

capacitor Device consisting of two conducting surfaces separated by an insulating material (dielectric) that stores electrical charge. It blocks dc, but passes ac. See *capacitance, impedance.*

cathode-ray tube (CRT) Funnel-shaped vacuum tube, in which a beam of electrons from an *electron gun* in the narrow end is directed at a phosphor screen in the wide end. The beam is controlled by electric or magnetic fields, so that it "writes" on the phosphor screen, which glows where the electrons strike it. See *electron gun.*

CMOS See *complementary metal oxide semiconductor logic.*

CMR See *common-mode rejection.*

color code Colored markings on some passive components to indicate value, tolerance, and so on.

common-mode rejection (CMR) See *differential amplifier.*

complementary metal oxide semiconductor logic (CMOS) Digital unipolar circuit with circuit voltages:

$$\begin{array}{ll} V_{DD} & 4 - 15 \text{ V} \\ \text{Low (0)} & 0 - 30\% \text{ of } V_{DD} \\ \text{High (1)} & 70\% \text{ of } V_{DD} \text{ to } V_{DD} \end{array}$$

coulomb (C) The quantity of electricity transported in 1 second by a current of 1 ampere (6.281×10^{18} electrons).

counter An arrangement of flip-flops that stores a binary number which increases in value by one each time an input pulse is received.

CRT See *cathode-ray tube.*

DAC See *digital-to-analog converter.*

dB See *decibel.*

dc See *direct current.*

decibel (dB) One-tenth of a bel, logarithmic unit for expressing ratio between two amounts of power, voltage, or current: dB = 10 $\log_{10}$ (P_1/P_2); dB = 20 $\log_{10}$ (V_1/V_2); dB = 20 $\log_{10}$ (I_1/I_2).

decoder 1. Circuit that converts binary numbers to decimal to be shown on a *seven-segment numeric display.* 2. *Demultiplexer.*

demultiplexer Device used to separate two or more signals that were previously combined by a *multiplexer* and transmitted via a single channel. Also called a *decoder.*

difference amplifier Operational amplifier circuit whose output equals the difference between two input voltages. Also called a *subtractor.*

differential amplifier Amplifier having two similar input circuits so connected that it responds to the difference between two voltages or currents applied to them, but effectively suppresses like voltages or currents. This property is called common-mode rejection (CMR).

digital circuit Circuit in which electrical signals consist of the presence or absence of discrete voltages, corresponding to the 1s and 0s of the binary number system.

digital multimeter (DMM) An instrument that measures dc volts, ac volts, ohms, dc milliamperes, and ac milliamperes, and displays the measured value in numerical form. Some DMMs have additional functions.

digital-to-analog converter (DAC) Device that converts digital data to analog form.

diode A semiconductor device, or electron tube, with two terminals that conducts electric current in one direction only. Used for rectification or switching. The two terminals are the anode and the cathode. When the anode is positive with respect to the cathode, the diode is forward biased, and current can flow; when the opposite is the case, current is blocked. See *zener diode, light emitting diode.*

diode bridge A full-wave rectifier consisting of four diodes, usually manufactured as an integrated circuit.

DIP See *dual in-line package.*

direct current (dc) A current that flows in one direction only. It may be continuous or pulsating, constant or varying, as long as its polarity does not change.

DMM See *digital multimeter.*

dual in-line package (DIP) Widely used packaging style for integrated circuits, in which the chip is encapsulated in a small rectangular plastic case with connection pins protruding from the two long side⁻. Pins are placed 0.1 inch apart to fit the holes of printed circuit boards, sockets, and so on.

EEPROM Electrically erasable programmable read-only memory, in which floating gate cells allow 1 bits to be stored by tunneling electrons using a gate potential of 20 V. The data can be erased in the same way, and new data written in. Also called EEROM, EAROM. See *read-only memory.*

effective voltage or current See *root-mean-square voltage or current.*

electron gun Cathode-ray tube device with indirectly heated cathode that emits electrons. The electrons are then shaped into a beam and accelerated by several electrodes. See *cathode-ray tube.*

encoder Circuit that converts decimal numbers entered via a keyboard to binary numbers.

EPROM Erasable programmable read-only memory, in which floating gate cells allow 1 bits to be stored by tunneling electrons, using a gate potential of 20 V. The data can be erased by exposure to ultraviolet light, and the memory can then be reprogrammed. Also called EROM. See *read-only memory.*

farad (F) The capacitance of a capacitor in which a charge of 1 coulomb results in a potential difference between its plates of 1 volt.

FET See *field-effect transistor.*

field-effect transistor (FET) Transistor in which conduction is by only one type of charge carrier (electrons *or* holes). In a junction FET (JFET) the gate is insulated from the channel by a depletion layer. In a metal-oxide semiconductor FET (MOSFET) the junction is replaced by a very thin layer of silicon dioxide.

filter Network of resistors, capacitors, inductors, or operational amplifiers that passes some frequencies while blocking others.

filter capacitor Capacitor used in a filter circuit, especially in a power supply.

flip-flop A circuit that can be in either of two states (output high or output low). It changes its state upon application of an input signal or clock pulse (gating signal). Also called a bistable *multivibrator* or *latch.*

frequency (*f*) Number of repetitions per second of a complete cycle of ac (audio, radio, etc.), expressed in *hertz (Hz).*

function generator Test instrument that generates square, triangle, and sine waves at various frequencies and amplitudes; some function generators also produce pulses with variable duty cycles.

gate Digital circuit consisting of transistor switches. See *inverter, AND gate, OR gate, NAND gate, NOR gate.*

germanium (Ge) Semiconductor element used in fabrication of *diodes* and *transistors.*

henry (H) The unit of inductance of a closed circuit in which an electromotive force of 1 volt is produced when the electric current in the circuit varies uniformly at a rate of 1 ampere per second.

hertz (Hz) The unit of frequency. One complete cycle per second of a recurrent waveform = 1 hertz.

impedance (Z) The total opposition (resistance (R) and reactance (X), both in ohms) that a circuit offers to ac at a given frequency: $Z = \sqrt{R^2 + X^2}$. See *resistance* and *reactance.*

inductance (L) Full name, *self-inductance.* When a current flowing in a conductor changes, the magnetic field around the conductor changes accordingly. This change, in turn, induces a current in the conductor itself that opposes the original current. Inductance is therefore mostly a phenomenon of ac flowing in inductors (for instance, coils). See *reactance.*

integrated circuit (IC) An array of active and passive components fabricated by various techniques (such as photoetching) on a semiconductor substrate (most often silicon). ICs are classified as follows.

Small-scale integration (SSI):	up to 12 gates
Medium-scale integration (MSI):	12–100 gates
Large-scale integration (LSI):	100–1,000 gates
Very large-scale integration (VLSI):	over 1,000 gates

integrator Circuit with an output proportional to the integral of the input.

inverter Logic gate in which the output is inverted with respect to the input: $A = \bar{Q}$. Also called a *NOT gate.*

JFET See *field-effect transistor.*

junction Region of transition between *n-type* and *p-type semiconductors* in diodes and junction transistors.

kilohm (kΩ) One thousand ohms $(1 \times 10^3 \ \Omega)$.

latch Flip-flop used for storing data, in which the logic state is retained by cross-coupled feedback loops. See *flip-flop.*

LCD See *liquid crystal display.*

LED See *light emitting diode.*

light emitting diode (LED) Gallium arsenide diode that emits light when forward biased with a specified current. LEDs are available with emissions in red, yellow, green, and infrared wavelengths.

liquid crystal display (LCD) A numeric or alphanumeric display in which figures or letters are formed by electric fields induced in a liquid crystal, a substance having both solid and liquid properties.

logarithmic amplifier Operational amplifier circuit, whose output is the logarithm of its input.

majority carrier Predominant charge carrier in a semiconductor (electrons in *n*-type, holes in *p*-type).

megohm (MΩ) One million ohms ($1 \times 10^6 \ \Omega$).

meter Any measuring device, but usually meaning one with a dial and a pointer that reads against a scale (for example, voltmeter, ammeter, ohmmeter, and so on).

microfarad (μF) One millionth of a farad ($1 \times 10^{-6} \ F$).

microprocessor A central processor unit (CPU) in a single IC. It consists of a clock, a control unit (comprising program counter, instruction register, processor status word, and stack pointer), memory control, bus control, working register, arithmetic logic unit, and internal memory. In addition to its use in digital computers, the microprocessor is also used for industrial sequencing and machine tool control, point-of-sale terminals, traffic light controllers, and so on.

microvolt (μV) One millionth of a volt ($1 \times 10^{-6} \ V$).

milliampere (mA) One thousandth of an ampere ($1 \times 10^{-3} \ A$).

millivolt (mV) One thousandth of a volt ($1 \times 10^{-3} \ V$).

milliwatt (mW) One thousandth of a watt ($1 \times 10^{-3} \ W$).

minority carrier Less predominant charge carrier in a semiconductor (electrons in *p*-type, holes in *n*-type).

MOSFET See *field-effect transistor.*

multiplexer Device for transmitting two or more signals simultaneously over a common transmission channel.

multiplier Operational amplifier circuit whose output is the product of two input signals.

multivibrator A resistance-capacitance oscillator, in which each of two transistors takes turns acting as a switch to turn the other on or off, so producing a square wave output. An *astable multivibrator* is an oscillator (free running). A *bistable multivibrator* is a flip-flop (toggle switch). A *monostable multivibrator* is a one-shot multivibrator (push button switch).

NAND gate Logic gate in which the output is low if both inputs are high: $AB = \bar{Q}$.

nanoampere (nA) One billionth of an ampere (1×10^{-9} A).

NOR gate Logic gate in which the output is low if either or both of the inputs are high: $A + B = \bar{Q}$.

NOT gate See *inverter.*

***n*-type semiconductor** Semiconductor with added impurities that donate free electrons.

ohm (Ω) The electric resistance between two points of a conductor when a constant difference of potential of 1 volt, applied between these two points, produces in this conductor a current of 1 ampere, this conductor not being the source of any electromotive force.

operational amplifier (op-amp) High-gain dc amplifier that depends on external feedback to determine its functional role.

optical isolator A device consisting of an optical emitter, such as an LED, and an optical detector, such as a phototransistor, in which the optical emitter causes the phototransistor to conduct when the optical emitter is excited. This device can be used as a coupler or a switch. Also called an optocoupler.

OR gate Logic gate in which the output is high if either, or both, of the inputs are high: $A + B = Q.$

PCB See *printed circuit board.*

peak inverse voltage (PIV) Maximum peak voltage that a diode can withstand in the reverse direction.

phase detector Circuit that compares the phases of two signals and generates a dc error voltage in proportion to any difference.

phase-locked loop (PLL) Circuit consisting of a *phase detector* and a *voltage-controlled oscillator*. An error signal from the phase detector changes the frequency of the voltage-controlled oscillator to agree with that of the input signal.

picofarad (pF) One trillionth of a farad (1×10^{-12} F).

PIV See *peak inverse voltage.*

PLL See *phase-locked loop.*

potentiometer (pot) See *resistor, variable.*

power supply Energy source that provides power for operating electronic equipment. A power supply may be a battery, an electronic unit that changes ac to dc, or a solar cell array.

preferred values Passive component series of values in which the increase between any two steps is the same percentage as between all the other steps. Increases are generally in steps of 5, 10, or 20 percent of the nominal value.

printed circuit board (PCB) An insulating board or card on which a pattern of metal conductors has been formed by etching or deposition, to connect together components attached to the other side of the board. The components are attached by inserting their leads through punched holes, and soldering them to the conductor pattern on the opposite side.

PROM Programmable read-only memory, in which 1s or 0s are permanently stored in the memory cells by preserving or blowing open microscopic fusible connections. This memory is programmed after fabrication and cannot be reprogrammed. See *read-only memory.*

p-**type semiconductor** Semiconductor with added impurities that create additional holes.

pulse A pulse is an abrupt change of the level (amplitude) of a baseline voltage for a limited period, after which it returns abruptly to the baseline. Pulses have pulse repetition rate (PRR), pulse amplitude, and pulse width. The ratio of the pulse width to the pulse period is called the duty cycle.

pulse generator Test instrument that generates pulses of various repetition rates, amplitudes, and duty cycles.

RAM See *random-access memory.*

random-access memory (RAM) Arrangement of memory cells that can be accessed directly, regardless of where they are located. A *dynamic RAM* has memory cells that each store four or more data bits as charges in minute capacitors that have to be refreshed at frequent intervals. A *static RAM* uses flip-flops for memory cells. These do not need refreshing, but take up more room on the chip. Both types of RAM are organized in a square pattern of rows and columns. Part of the memory address selects the row, part selects the column.

reactance (*X*) Opposition to the flow of ac. *Capacitive reactance* (X_C) is opposition due to capacitance; *inductive reactance* (X_L) is opposition due to inductance. Both are measured in ohms, and respectively decrease or increase with frequency: $X_C = 1/2\,\pi f C$, where *f* is the frequency in hertz and *C* the capacitance in farads; $X_L = 2\pi f L$, where *L* is the inductance in henries. [$2\pi = 6.283$ approximately]

read-only memory (ROM) This memory stores permanent data, which are not lost when powered down. Connections to the internal transistors that determine whether the cell is storing a 1 or a 0 are made using a masking process during fabrication and cannot be altered. See also *PROM, EPROM, EEPROM.*

rectification 1. Half-wave rectification consists of blocking all the negative peaks of the ac, leaving only the positive peaks (or vice versa). 2. Full-wave rectification consists of reversing the polarity of the negative peaks so that all peaks are positive (or vice versa).

rectifier Diode used to convert ac to dc. The important parameters are: maximum peak inverse voltage (PIV); maximum forward voltage drop (V_F); maximum forward current (I_F); maximum surge current; maximum reverse current at PIV.

register Arrangement of flip-flops for temporary storage of binary data.

regulation In a power supply, the ability to maintain a constant output voltage or current despite variations of line voltage or load impedance.

regulator circuit Circuit that enables a power supply to deliver a constant voltage or current to a load regardless of variations of line voltage or load impedance. See *zener regulator, three-terminal regulator, switching regulator.*

resistance (*R*) Property of a substance that impedes current and results in the dissipation of power as heat. The unit of resistance is the ohm (Ω).

resistive ladder network An array of resistors that converts a binary input to an analog output.

resistor, fixed Passive component made of a material (like carbon or high-resistance wire) that has a specific resistance, used to limit current or provide a voltage drop. See *color code, resistance.*

resistor, variable Three-terminal resistor provided with a sliding tap that can be moved along it in such a way that the resistance between the tap and either end of the resistive element can be varied. Also called a *potentiometer* or a *rheostat.*

rheostat Variable resistor, generally wirewound, with two terminals (one end of the resistive element and a sliding tap).

ROM See *read-only memory.*

root-mean-square (rms) voltage or current The square root of the average of all the values of a periodic quantity taken throughout one complete period, also called the *effective value.*

$$V_{rms} = \sqrt{\frac{1}{2\pi} \int_0^{2\pi} v^2 d(\omega t)}$$

where v = peak voltage and $\omega = 2\pi f$. In the case of a sine waves;

$$V_{rms} = 0.707 \ V_{pk}.$$

semiconductor A material having electrical properties between those of conductors and insulators, such as *silicon, germanium,* and so on.

seven-segment numeric display LED or LCD display consisting of seven bars so arranged that each decimal digit from 0 to 9 can be displayed by energizing two or more.

silicon (Si) Semiconductor element used for fabrication of *diodes, transistors, integrated circuits,* and so on.

square wave generator Free-running *multivibrator* with symmetrical output (positive and negative excursions of waveform are equal).

summing amplifier Operational amplifier whose output equals the sum of its inputs.

switching regulator Circuit that generates pulses that have a pulse width that varies in proportion to the power supply output voltage. The pulses control the on time of the series pass transistor, so regulating the output.

T See *tesla.*

tesla (T) Unit of magnetic flux density ($T = Wb/m^2$).

thermistor Type of resistor whose resistance decreases as its temperature rises.

three-terminal regulator IC containing a *regulator circuit.*

time constant In a capacitor-resistor series circuit, the time in seconds required for the capacitor to reach 63.2 percent of its full charge after a voltage is applied.

timer Circuit that emits a signal after a specific delay time. The same circuit can be adapted to generate clock pulses.

transformer Device in which ac in one winding induces ac in another. The windings may be wound on an iron core, or on no core (air core), and are designated primary and secondary respectively. The ratio (T) between the number of turns in the primary winding (N_p) and the number of turns in the secondary winding (N_s) determines the voltage, current, and impedance of each: $V_p/V_s = N_p/N_s$; $I_p/I_s = N_s/N_p$; $T = N_p/N_s$ or N_s/N_p; $Z = T^2$.

transistor Three-terminal semiconductor device used for switching or amplification. See *bipolar junction transistor, field-effect transistor.*

transistor-transistor logic (TTL) Digital bipolar circuits with circuit voltages:

V_{cc}	5.00 ± 0.25 V
Low (0) input	0 to 0.8 V
Low (0) output	0 to 0.4 V
High (1) input	2.0 to 5.0 V
High (1) output	2.4 to 5.0 V

truth table Table showing all output logic levels consequent upon all possible logic inputs to a digital device.

TTL See *transistor-transistor logic.*

valence electrons Electrons in the outer atomic shells of elements such as silicon and germanium that lock together with those in neighboring atoms to form a crystal lattice. This behavior is called covalent bonding.

VCO See *voltage-controlled oscillator.*

volt (V) The difference of electric potential between two points of a conducting wire carrying a constant current of 1 ampere, when the power dissipated between those points is equal to 1 watt. (V = W/A)

voltage comparator Operational amplifier in open-loop circuit. Output changes from false to true when analog input voltage level exceeds reference voltage and vice versa.

voltage-controlled oscillator (VCO) Oscillator in which the frequency is varied by varying an applied voltage.

volt-ohm-milliammeter (VOM) See *analog multitester.*

wavelength (λ) The length of one complete cycle of ac. For electromagnetic waves, it is given by $\lambda = c/f$, where λ is the wavelength in meters, c is the velocity of light in a vacuum (= 2.99796 × 10^8 m/s), and f is the frequency in hertz. (For other waves it is given by $\lambda = v/f$, where v is the velocity in meters per second.)

Wb See *weber.*

weber (Wb) The magnetic flux which, linking a circuit of one turn, produces in it an electromotive force of 1 volt as it is reduced to zero at a uniform rate in 1 second.

zener diode A diode that has a very sharp, nondestructive breakdown in its reverse-bias region. The voltage at which this takes place is used to establish a reference voltage, and is called the breakdown voltage, $V_{Z,nom}$. Other parameters include:

minimum current necessary for operation (also called the knee current)	I_{ZK}
maximum current that can flow in the diode	I_{ZM}
test current	I_{ZT}
zener impedance	Z_Z

zener regulator Power supply regulator circuit that uses a *zener diode* for reference.

INDEX

INDEX